COLLECTION 1

Kristy and her friends love babysitting and when her mum can't find a babysitter for Kristy's little brother one day, Kristy has a great idea. Why doesn't she set up a babysitting club? That way parents can make a single phone call and reach a team of babysitting experts. And if one babysitter is already busy another one can take the job. So together with her friends, Claudia, Mary Anne and Stacey, Kristy starts THE BABYSITTERS CLUB. And although things don't *always* go according to plan, they have a lot of fun on the way!

COLLECTION 1

Book 1
KRISTY'S GREAT IDEA

Book 2
CLAUDIA AND THE
PHANTOM PHONE CALLS

Book 3
THE TRUTH ABOUT STACEY

Ann M. Martin

Scholastic Children's Books,
Commonwealth House, 1 – 19 New Oxford Street,
London, WC1A 1NU, UK
A division of Scholastic Ltd
London ~ New York ~ Toronto ~ Sydney ~ Auckland

Kristy's Great Idea
Claudia and the Phantom Phone Calls
The Truth About Stacey
First published in the US by Scholastic Inc., 1986
First published in the UK by Scholastic Ltd, 1988
First published in this edition by Scholastic Ltd, 1998

ISBN 0 590 19877 7

Typeset by Rowland Phototypesetting Ltd,
Bury St Edmunds, Suffolk
Printed by Cox & Wyman Ltd, Reading, Berks.

1 2 3 4 5 6 7 8 9 10

CONTENTS

KRISTY'S GREAT IDEA

We dug into the pizza while Mum started making phone calls.

She called Mary Anne. Mary Anne was sitting for the Pikes.

She called Claudia. Claudia had an art class.

She called two high school girls. They had cheerleading practice.

David Michael looked like he might cry.

Finally Mum called Mrs Newton and asked if she would mind if I brought David Michael with me when I sat for Jamie. Luckily, Mrs Newton didn't mind.

I chewed away at a gloppy mouthful of cheese and pepperoni and thought it was too bad that Mum's pizza had to get cold while she made all those phone calls. I thought it was too bad that David Michael had to sit there and feel he was causing a lot of trouble just because he was only six years old and couldn't take care of himself yet.

Then the idea for the Babysitters Club came to me and I almost choked.

I could barely wait until nine o'clock so I could signal the great idea to Mary Anne.

KRISTY'S GREAT IDEA

This book is for Beth McKeever Perkins,
my old babysitting buddy.
With love (and years of memories).

1st
CHAPTER

The Babysitters Club. I'm proud to say it was totally my idea, even though the four of us worked it out together. "Us" is Mary Anne Spier, Claudia Kishi, Stacey McGill, and me—Kristy Thomas.

I got the idea on the first Tuesday afternoon of the autumn term. It was a very hot day. It was so hot that in my un-air-conditioned school, Stoneybrook Middle School, the teachers had opened every single window and door and turned off all the lights. My hair stuck damply to the back of my neck, and I wished I had a rubber band so I could pull it into a long ponytail. Bees flew into the classroom and droned round our heads, and Mr Redmont, our teacher, let us stop working to make fans out of cartridge paper. The fans didn't do much except keep the bees away, but it was nice to take up ten minutes of geography making them.

Anyway, that stifling afternoon dragged on for ever, and when the hands of the clock on the front wall of our classroom finally hit 2.42 and the bell rang, I leaped out of my seat and shouted, "Hurray!" I was just so glad that it was time to get out of there. I like school and everything, but sometimes enough is enough.

Mr Redmont looked shocked. He was probably thinking he'd been so nice letting us make fans and there I was, not appreciating it at all, just glad the day was over.

I felt bad, but I couldn't help what I'd done. I'm like that. I think of something to say, and say it. I think of something to do, and I do it. Mum calls it impulsive. Sometimes she calls it trouble. But she doesn't just mean trouble. She means *trouble*.

And I was in trouble then. I could sense it. I've been in enough trouble to know when it's coming.

Mr Redmont cleared his throat. He was trying to think of a way to punish me without humiliating me in front of the other kids. Things like that are important to him.

"Kristy," Mr Redmont began, and then he changed his mind and started again. "Class," he said, "you have your homework. You may go. Kristy, I'd like to see you for a minute."

While the rest of the kids gathered up their books and papers and left the room, talking and giggling, I made my way up to

6

Mr Redmont's desk. Before he could say a word, I began apologizing to him. Sometimes that helps.

"Mr Redmont," I said, "I'm really sorry. I didn't mean anything. I mean, I didn't mean I was glad school was over. I meant I was glad I could go home. Because my house is air-conditioned . . ."

Mr Redmont nodded. "But do you think, Kristy, that it would be possible, in the future, for you to conduct yourself with a bit more decorum?"

I wasn't sure of the exact meaning of *decorum*, but I had a pretty good idea it meant not spoiling Mr Redmont's day by jumping up and shouting hurray when the bell rang.

"Yes, sir," I said. Sometimes being polite also helps.

"Good," said Mr Redmont. "But I want you to remember this incident, and the best way for us to remember things is to write them down. So tonight, I would like you to write a five-hundred-word essay on the importance of decorum in the classroom."

Darn. I'd have to find out what *decorum* meant after all.

"Yes, sir," I said again.

I went back to my desk, gathered up my books very slowly, and then walked very slowly out of the classroom. I hoped Mr Redmont was noticing the slowness because I was betting it was an important part of decorum.

I found Mary Anne Spier waiting for me outside the door to my classroom. She was leaning against the wall, biting her nails.

Mary Anne is my best friend. We live next door to each other. We even look a little alike. We're both small for our age and we both have brown hair that falls past our shoulders. But that's where the similarity ends, because I can't keep my mouth shut, and Mary Anne is very quiet and very shy. Luckily, that's only on the outside. The people who know her well, like Claudia and Stacey and me, see the inside of her, and the Mary Anne who's hiding in there is a lot of fun.

"Hey," I greeted her. I pulled her hand out of her mouth and looked at her nails. "Mary Anne! How do you ever expect to be able to wear nail polish if you keep doing that?"

"Oh, come on," she said with a sigh. "Nail polish. I'll be seventy-five before my father lets me wear it."

Mary Anne's father is the only family she's got. Her mother is dead, and she has no brothers or sisters. Unfortunately, her father is pretty strict. My mother says it's just because Mr Spier is nervous since Mary Anne is all he's got. You'd think, though, that he could let her wear her hair down instead of always in plaits, or give her permission to ride her bike to the mall with

Claudia and me once in a while. But, no. At Mr Spier's house it's rules, rules, rules. It's a miracle that Mary Anne was even allowed to become a member of the Babysitters Club.

We walked out of school, and suddenly I began running. I forgot all about decorum, because I'd just remembered something else. "Oh, gosh!" I cried.

Mary Anne raced after me. "What is it?" she panted.

"It's Tuesday," I called over my shoulder.

"So? Slow down, Kristy. It's too hot to run."

"I can't slow down. Tuesday is my afternoon to watch David Michael. I'm supposed to beat him home. Otherwise he gets home first and has to watch himself."

David Michael is my six-year-old brother. My big brothers, Charlie and Sam, and I are each responsible for him one afternoon a week until Mum gets home from work. Kathy, this fifteen-year-old girl who lives a few blocks from us, watches him the other two afternoons. Kathy gets paid to watch him. Charlie and Sam and I don't.

Mary Anne and I ran all the way home. We reached my front yard, sweaty and out of breath. And there was David Michael, sitting forlornly on the front steps, his dark curls falling limply across his forehead.

He burst into tears as soon as he saw us. "What's wrong?" I asked. I sat down beside him and put my arm around his shoulders.

"I'm locked out," he wailed.

"What happened to your key?"

David Michael shook his head. "I don't know." He wiped his eyes, hiccupping.

"Well," I said, "it's all right." I got my own key out of my bag.

David Michael burst into fresh tears. "No, it's not! It's not all right. I couldn't get in and I have to go to the bathroom."

I unlocked the door. When David Michael gets like this, it's best just to sort of ignore his tears and pretend everything is fine.

Mary Anne and I held the door open for him and I ushered him into the bathroom. Our collie Louie tore outside as we went in. He was frantic to get outdoors after being locked in the house since breakfast time.

"While you go to the bathroom," I told David Michael, "I'm going to get us some lemonade, okay?"

David Michael actually smiled. "Okay!"

I'm good with children. So is Mary Anne. Mum says so. Both of us get lots of afternoon and weekend baby-sitting jobs. In fact, I'd been offered a job for that afternoon, but I had to turn it down because of David Michael.

That reminded me. "Hey," I said to Mary Anne as I turned on the air condition-ing, "Mrs Newton asked me to baby-sit for

Jamie this afternoon. Didn't she call you after she called me?"

Mary Anne sat down at the kitchen table and watched me put lemonade in a big glass jug. She shook her head. "No. Maybe she called Claudia."

Claudia Kishi lives across the street from me. She and Mary Anne and I have lived in Bradford Court since we were born. We've grown up together, but somehow Claudia has never spent as much time with us as Mary Anne and I have spent with each other. For one thing, Claudia's really into art and always off at art classes, or else holed up in her room painting or drawing. Or reading mysteries. That's her other passion. She's much more grown-up than Mary Anne and I. When we were little, Mary Anne and I were always playing schools or dolls or dressing-up, but we practically had to brainwash Claudia to get her to join us. A lot of the time, we just didn't bother, but Claudia's always been good for a bike ride or going to the pictures or the swimming pool. As far as I'm concerned, one of the best things about Claudia is that her father isn't Mr Spier. Mr Kishi can be strict about Claudia's schoolwork, but he doesn't faint if you suggest going downtown for a Coke or something.

Still, Claudia has never been a close friend, and this year, the gap between us seems to have widened, since school started.

Even though we're all in the top class, Claudia suddenly seems . . . older. She talks about boys, and spends most of her time adding to her wardrobe and talking on the phone. In the short time since school started, she's become a different person.

David Michael came into the kitchen looking much cheerier.

"Here you go," I said. I handed him a glass of lemonade as he sat next to Mary Anne.

Charlie came in then, tossing a football around. Sam got home a few minutes later, with our collie Louie skidding along behind him. Charlie is sixteen and Sam is fourteen. They both go to Stoneybrook High.

"Hi, everybody. Hi, squirt," Charlie said to David Michael.

"I am not a squirt," replied David Michael.

Charlie thought he was so great because he'd just made the school team. You'd think he was the first person ever to play football for Stoneybrook High.

"We're going to play ball in the Hansons' backyard," Sam announced. "Want to play, Kristy?"

I did, but David Michael wouldn't want to. He was too little. "I don't know. I thought Mary Anne and I would take David Michael to the brook. Do you want to go wading, David Michael?" I asked.

He nodded happily.

"See you later," I called as Sam and Charlie left the house, slamming the front door behind them.

Mary Anne and I took David Michael and Louie to the brook. We watched David Michael wade and make sailboats and try to catch minnows. Louie ran round, looking for squirrels.

"I'd better go," Mary Anne said after an hour or so. "Dad will be home soon."

"Yeah. Mum will be home soon, too. David Michael," I called, "time to leave."

He stood up reluctantly and the three of us and Louie walked home together.

When we reached our drive, David Michael ran across the lawn, and Mary Anne whispered to me, "Nine o'clock, okay?"

I grinned. "Okay." Mary Anne and I had a secret code. Mary Anne made it up. We can signal to each other with torches. If I look out of my bedroom window I can see right into hers. Lots of nights we talk to each other with the torches, since Mary Anne isn't allowed to phone after dinner except for things like baby-sitting jobs or getting homework.

When Mum came home a little while later, she had a pizza with her. My brothers and I stood round the kitchen breathing in the smell of cheese and pepperoni.

But Sam and Charlie looked sceptical. "I wonder what she wants," murmured Sam.

"Yeah," said Charlie.

Mum only gets pizza when she has to ask us a favour.

I decided not to beat about the bush. "How come you bought a pizza, Mum?" I asked.

Charlie kicked my ankle, but I ignored him. "Come on. What do you have to ask us?"

Mum grinned. She knew exactly what she was doing. And she knew that we knew it. "Oh, all right," she said. "Kathy called me at work to say she won't be able to watch David Michael tomorrow. I was wondering what you are—"

"Football practice," said Charlie promptly.

"Maths Club," said Sam.

"Sitting at the Newtons'," I said.

"Drat," said Mum.

"But we *are* sorry," added Sam.

"I know you are."

Then we dug into the pizza while Mum started making phone calls.

She called Mary Anne. Mary Anne was sitting for the Pikes.

She called Claudia. Claudia had an art class.

She called two high school girls. They had cheerleading practice.

David Michael looked like he might cry.

Finally Mum called Mrs Newton and asked if she would mind if I brought David

Michael with me when I sat for Jamie. Luckily, Mrs Newton didn't mind.

I chewed away at a gloppy mouthful of cheese and pepperoni and thought it was too bad that Mum's pizza had to get cold while she made all those phone calls. I thought it was too bad that David Michael had to sit there and feel he was causing a lot of trouble just because he was only six years old and couldn't take care of himself yet.

Then the idea for the Babysitters Club came to me and I almost choked.

I could barely wait until nine o'clock so I could signal the great idea to Mary Anne.

2nd CHAPTER

After dinner that night I went to my bedroom and shut my door. Then I sat down at my desk with a pad of paper and a sharpened pencil. I had three things to do: the composition on decorum, my homework, and some thinking about the Babysitters Club. I planned to do them in that order, worst first.

I looked up *decorum* in my dictionary. It said: "Conformity to social conventions; propriety. See Synonyms at *etiquette*." I had to look up both *propriety* and *etiquette* before I got the picture. Then I understood. I'd been rude. Why hadn't Mr Redmont just said so? It would have made things a lot simpler. So I wrote down some stuff about how being rude was distracting to other students and made Stoneybrook Middle School look bad to visitors. I counted the words. Four hundred and ninety-eight. So I added "The End" with a great big flourish and hoped for the best.

Then I did the maths homework and read about Paraguay for geography.

And *then* it was time to think about the Babysitters Club.

I smoothed out a fresh piece of paper and started making a list:

> *1. Members:*
>   *Me*
>   *Mary Anne*
>   *Claudia*
>   *Who else?*
>
> *2. Advertising:*
>   *Fliers*
>   *Telephone*
>   *Newspaper?*
>
> *3. Set up meeting times when clients*
>   *can call to line up sitters.*
>   *Where to meet?*
>
> *4. Weekly subs for expenses?*

My idea was that Mary Anne and Claudia and I would form a club to do baby-sitting. We would tell people (our clients) that at certain times during the week we could all be reached at one number. We would hold our meetings during those times. That way, when someone needed a sitter, he or she could make one phone call and reach three different people. One of us would be available for sure. Of course, people could call us individually at other times, but the beauty of the meetings would be the opportunity to reach several baby-sitters at once. That way, our clients wouldn't have to go through what Mum had just gone through at dinner.

We would have to advertise ourselves, I decided. I was hoping Claudia would help us make up some fliers to stick in the letterboxes in our neighbourhood. She'd be able to draw something really cute on our ads.

I looked at my watch. It was a quarter to nine. Fifteen more minutes before I was supposed to signal Mary Anne. I was getting edgy. I had such a terrific idea and I couldn't even pick up the phone like a normal human being to tell Mary Anne about it. Mr Spier would just tell me I could see Mary Anne in school tomorrow.

I sighed.

Mum knocked on my door. I knew it was Mum because none of my brothers ever bothers to knock. They just barge in.

"Come in," I called.

"Hi, sweetie," said Mum. She closed the door behind her and sat on the edge of my bed. "How was school?"

Mum tries to spend a little time alone with each of us kids every day. She feels guilty that she and my father are divorced and that she has to work full-time to support us. She's told us so. I wish she wouldn't feel guilty. It's not her fault that Dad ran off to California and got married again and doesn't send Mum much child support money. Mum says she doesn't want more money, though. She has a terrific job at this big company in Stamford, and she likes the fact that she can support us so well. It makes her feel proud and independent. But she still feels guilty.

My father can be a jerk sometimes. He hasn't called us for over a year. And he even forgot my twelfth birthday last month.

I paused, trying to think of a way to answer Mum's question without telling her about the composition I'd had to write.

"Kristy?" Mum asked.

"It was fine."

"Okay, what happened?"

There is absolutely no fooling Mum.

"Well," I said, "you know how hot it was today?"

"Yes."

"And you know how sometimes a hot day can seem really long?"

"Kristy, get to the point."

So I did. And Mum laughed. Then she read my composition and said she thought it was fine. I asked her if she thought "The End" could count as the four hundred and ninety-ninth and five-hundredth words, and she smiled and said she hoped so.

My mum is really great.

When she left to go and talk to Sam, it was nine o'clock.

I got out my torch, turned off the lamp by my desk, and stood at the window that faced Mary Anne's room.

I flashed the light once to let her know I was there.

She flashed back. Good, she was ready.

Then I flashed out this message (it took for ever):

HAVE GREAT IDEA FOR BABYSITTERS CLUB. MUST TALK. IMPORTANT. CAN'T WAIT. WE CAN GET LOTS OF JOBS.

There was a pause. Then Mary Anne flashed: WHAT? and I had to start all over again. I shortened the message. At last Mary Anne flashed: TERRIFIC. SEE YOU TOMORROW. And we put the torches away. Mary Anne hasn't been caught once and we plan to keep it that way.

I was just closing the drawer where I hide my torch, when Mum knocked again.

"Come in," I said curiously, turning the light on. Mum doesn't usually come back for a second chat. On the other hand, I don't usually keep my door closed for so long.

This time, Mum sat at my desk and I sat on the bed.

"I just wanted to let you know," she said, "that I'm going out with Watson on Saturday night. I forgot to tell you before."

I groaned. Mum has been seeing this

20

man, Watson, off and on for about four months. She likes him a lot, but I don't like him much at all. He's divorced from his wife and has two little kids. Plus, he's getting bald.

"I'm not asking for your permission, Kristy," Mum said. "I just want you to be able to plan on my being out on Saturday. Charlie's got a date, but Sam will be at home."

I nodded.

"I wish you could be a little more open-minded about Watson," said Mum. "I can't make you like him, but you haven't given him much of a chance."

The truth is, I haven't given any of the men Mum has dated a chance. I'm afraid that if I break down and treat them nicely, one of them might marry Mum. Think what could happen then. We're happy the way we are.

"One more thing," said Mum. "This is Watson's weekend to have the children and he has to work on Saturday morning. He doesn't like it, but that's the way it is. He wondered if you'd baby-sit for Andrew and Karen while he's at the office."

I shook my head. Watson had asked me at least three times to sit for his kids, but I won't do it. I don't want to have anything to do with him or his family. I either make up an excuse or else I flatly refuse.

"Okay," said Mum. "It's your choice."

She sounded as if she meant, It's your funeral.

But she came over to me and kissed the top of my head, so I knew she wasn't angry.

"Going to bed soon?" she asked.

"Yeah. You can leave the door open," I told her as she left my room.

I said goodnight to my brothers, and half an hour later I crawled into bed. Louie settled down next to me. I lay there stroking him and thinking about Mum and Watson and Andrew and Karen. Then I remembered the Babysitters Club and cheered up.

Tomorrow couldn't come fast enough!

3rd CHAPTER

Mr Redmont accepted my composition on decorum. I handed it to him before school, so he wouldn't have to read it while the entire class was hanging around. He didn't count the words, just skimmed it, looked up at me, and said, "This is fine, Kristy. Fine work. You express yourself very nicely on paper."

And that was it. No words of wisdom, no scolding.

I heaved a sigh of relief and walked to my desk with decorum.

After school, Mary Anne and I ran home together again. It wasn't quite as hot as it had been the day before, so we weren't as uncomfortable.

"You're sitting for the Pikes today?" I asked Mary Anne as we jogged along.

Mary Anne nodded.

"How many of them?" There are eight Pike children.

"Two, Claire and Margo."

"Oh, not bad," I said. Claire and Margo are four and six. They're fun. More importantly, they like baby-sitters.

"Where are you sitting today?" asked Mary Anne.

"The Newtons'. David Michael is coming with me. He can play with Jamie."

"Oh, hey, great! Maybe I'll bring Claire and Margo over for a while. They can all play together. And then you can tell me about the babysitting club."

"Okay!" I agreed.

We parted when we reached my house, and I was glad to see that I'd got home before David Michael. I let Louie out and made a jug of lemonade.

At 3.30 sharp, David Michael and I were standing on the Newtons' front steps. Punctuality is an important part of baby-sitting. I have never once been late for a job. My customers appreciate that.

I let David Michael ring the bell. In a few seconds the front door was flung wide open.

"Hi-hi!" exclaimed Jamie. Jamie is three.

David Michael gave me a look that said, I have to play with a three-year-old who goes *hi-hi*?

I patted David Michael on the back.

"Hi, Jamie," I replied.

"Look!" he exclaimed, as we stepped into

the Newtons' front hall. "Look what I got!" He held out a little doll in an army uniform. "It's a G.I. Joe."

"Really?" said David Michael, suddenly interested.

"Yup," said Jamie proudly.

"Got any others?" asked my little brother.

"Sure," replied Jamie. "Come on."

The boys ran off. Mrs Newton greeted me from the kitchen. "Thank goodness for G.I. Joe," she said.

I smiled. "Sorry about David Michael, but it looks like it'll work out okay." I never like to impose on my clients.

"I'm sure it will be fine." Mrs Newton patted her bulging stomach. "Jamie had better get used to other children."

"How long until the baby's due?" I asked.

"About eight weeks."

I sighed. "Oh, I wish it would hurry up!"

"*You* wish!"

Mrs Newton gave me the instructions for the afternoon. "Just the doctor's appointment and a few errands," she reminded me. "I should be back by five-thirty."

"Okay. Five-thirty," I repeated.

As soon as she was gone, I called Mary Anne at the Pikes'. "Come over whenever you want to," I said.

The Pikes live just a few doors away, so

Mary Anne showed up in ten minutes. She was pulling Claire and Margo in a red wagon.

"Hi-hi!" Jamie greeted them cheerfully.

"Hi-hi!" Claire, the four-year-old replied.

David Michael and Margo eyed each other suspiciously. They hadn't played together much, and David Michael was wary of any little girl, especially one who wasn't in his class at school.

We took the kids out to Jamie's swings. When they were playing happily, Mary Anne said, "So what about the baby-sitting club?"

"Well," I replied, "I thought we could get together with a couple of other girls who baby-sit and form a club—sort of like a company—"

We were interrupted by a thump and a wail.

Jamie had fallen off one of the swings.

"*Wahh!*" he cried.

I ran to him and checked him over. No bumps, no skinned knees.

"*Wahh!*"

"Where does it hurt?" I asked him.

He pointed to his tummy, then let his hand drift to his knee, and finally up to his head.

"Everywhere?" I suggested.

He nodded miserably.

"Maybe we'd better go," said Mary Anne, rounding up Claire and Margo.

"Okay," I replied. "Listen, why don't we tell Claudia the idea? Let's go over to her house when we've finished sitting. She'll be back from her art class then."

"Okay. See you."

Inside, I gave Jamie a biscuit, and he and David Michael played with the G.I. Joes and then watched *Sesame Street* on TV. Jamie's accident was long forgotten by the time his mother came home.

Mrs Newton paid me and I ran to my house, leaving David Michael with Sam, and then ran across the street to Claudia Kishi's.

Recently, I haven't felt quite as comfortable visiting Claudia as I used to. This year she had to go and start growing up faster than us. She's wearing a bra, and the way she talks, you'd think boys had just been invented.

She acts like all the guys in our class aren't the same goony boys they were last year. Last year, the boys were saying, "Want some ABC gum?" and then handing us the gum out of their mouths, saying, "It's Already-Been-Chewed, get it?" and laughing hysterically. Last year, the boys were throwing spitballs at us. Last year, the boys were pulling our chairs out from under us when we stood up to answer questions. *This* year (if you listen to Claudia), the boys are heroes. Personally, I don't see any change.

I rang the Kishis' bell. Claudia came to

the door. She was wearing short, very baggy lavender tartan overalls, a white lacy blouse, a black trilby, and red high-top sneakers without socks. Her long black hair was carefully arranged in four plaits. I felt extremely boring compared to her.

I was so used to seeing Claudia in outfits like that that I didn't bat an eye. What I did notice was that she was wearing make-up. There was blue stuff on her eyelids, gold stuff above her eyes, and magenta stuff on her cheeks.

"Claudia!" I gasped. "Your face! You look like"—I couldn't stop myself in time—"you got made up for the circus . . . I mean . . . it's so colourful . . ."

"Thanks a lot."

"No, honestly, Claud. You don't *need* make-up. You've got such a beautiful face . . ."

"Oh, you just think it's exotic," said Claudia.

Well, maybe I do. Claudia's parents are originally from Japan. They came to the United States when they were very young. Claudia has silky, jet-black hair, dark eyes, and creamy skin without so much as a trace of a pimple. She's absolutely gorgeous. But she has this wild streak in her that makes her buy belts made of feathers and wear knee socks with palm trees on them. Make-up was something new, though.

"Are you going to wear *that*"—I pointed

to her face—"to school tomorrow?"

"If I can get away with it."

I nodded. Claudia's parents are very conservative. They don't understand her taste in clothes at all. They're pretty nice about the trilbies and stuff, although they won't buy any of those things for her. (That's why she has to baby-sit—to earn money for all that stuff.) But I didn't know how the Kishis would react to Claudia's day-glo face. I didn't know how our teachers would react, either.

I said hello to Mimi, Claudia's grandmother, who was busy making dinner, and followed Claudia upstairs to her room. "Where's Janine?" I asked.

Claudia rolled her eyes. "At the university, where else?"

Janine is Claudia's fifteen-year-old sister. She's only in high school, but she's taking classes at Stoneybrook University. This is because Janine is a real live genius. An average person has an IQ of 100. An above average person has an IQ of 120 to 140. A person with an IQ of 160 is considered a genius.

Janine's IQ is 196.

Sometimes she makes me want to be sick. She almost always makes Claudia want to be sick. She thinks she knows everything. (Actually, she does.) She's forever correcting us. If I say, "David Michael, you can't play outside today because it's raining," Janine

29

will say, "Kristy, you should say, 'David Michael, you *may not* play outside today.' If you say he *can't*, it means he's physically unable to, and that's not true. What you mean is that he does not have *permission* to play out of doors."

Janine sounds like a textbook. Her best friend is this fourteen-year-old maths nerd who's going to leave high school in the spring. Her second best friend is her computer.

I'm sure it's because of Janine that Claudia concentrates on art and is a terrible student.

I was relieved to hear that Janine wasn't at home.

Claudia and I plopped down on her bed.

"Mary Anne'll be here in a few minutes," I said. "I have this really great idea that I want to tell both of you about."

Claudia's eyes lit up. "What is it?"

"A baby-sitters club," I announced.

"A baby-sitters club?" she squealed.

"Yeah, I'll explain it all when—" Just then, the doorbell rang.

Claudia thundered down the stairs, yelling "I'll get it!" She flung open the front door and hauled Mary Anne up to her room. "I like clubs!" she exclaimed. "Tell us your idea!"

"Well, it all started last night," I began. I told them how Mum had had to call nearly everyone in Stoneybrook, looking for a baby-sitter, and how long it had taken, and how bad David Michael had felt. "So I thought we could sort of join together. We all baby-sit anyway. We could advertise ourselves and get more customers. We should meet a few times each week and tell our customers what those times are. Then they can make one call and reach a whole bunch of us at once. And if, like, Mrs Pike wants *two* sitters, she'll only have to make one call." I explained everything else I had thought of, and wound up with, "Okay, here are two things to think about: One, where should we hold our meetings; and two, who else could we ask to join the club?"

"I can answer both questions," said Claudia. "We should hold the meetings here, because I have a phone in my room."

"Oh, terrific!" I exclaimed. (I'd been hoping Claudia would suggest that.)

"And I know someone who might want to join the club."

"Who?" Mary Anne and I asked.

"She's new. She's just moved to Stoney-brook. She lives in Fawcett Avenue, and she's in my class. Her name is Stacey McGill."

"Well, okay . . ." I said slowly. "Of course, we'll have to meet her."

"Oh, sure. You'll really like her. She's from New York City," Claudia added.

I was impressed. I could tell Mary Anne was, too. She opened her eyes wide. "I wonder why her family wanted to leave *there* and come *here*," she said.

Claudia shrugged. "Don't know. But I'm glad they did. Stacey's really cool."

Mary Anne and I glanced at each other, not sure that this was a good sign.

"What's everyone doing tomorrow afternoon?" asked Claudia. "Can we meet then?"

"If it's at five-thirty again," said Mary Anne. "I have to baby-sit before then."

We agreed to meet late the next afternoon. And that was how the Babysitters Club officially began.

4th CHAPTER

Promptly at 5.30 the next afternoon, I crossed the street to Claudia's house and rang the bell. Claudia answered it again, this time wearing a baggy yellow and black-checked shirt, black pants, red jazz shoes, and a bracelet that looked like it was made from a telephone cord. Her earrings were dangling jointed skeletons that jumped around when she moved. I noticed she wasn't wearing any make-up.

"Mum and Dad wouldn't let me," she said.

"Well, you got away with the skeletons."

Claudia grinned. "I didn't put those on until I got to school," she whispered. "Mimi's the only grown-up at home now and she doesn't mind if I wear skeletons."

"Oh, very sneaky!" Claudia knows every trick.

As we went up the stairs, Claudia said,

"Stacey's already here. I really hope you like her." She lowered her voice. "And Janine's home."

I groaned.

"Sorry. Her door's open, too."

At that moment, Janine stuck her head out into the hall. "Oh, hi, Kristy," she said. "I thought I heard voices. Claudia told me about the Babysitters Club. That sounds like an outstanding idea."

"Well, hopefully it will—" I began.

Janine's face took on her know-it-all look. "Kristy, *hopefully* is one of the most commonly misused words in the English language. The word means 'in a hopeful manner.' It is not acceptable to use it to mean 'it is to be hoped.' If I were—"

I didn't have the vaguest idea what she was talking about. "Gee, Janine, I gotta go," I cut her off as Claudia went on into her room. "Stacey's waiting for us. See you." I really cannot take much of Janine. And I *always* make a mistake in front of her. I don't know how Claudia manages to live in the same house with her.

Just as I reached Claudia's bedroom, the doorbell rang. "That's Mary Anne," I called. "I'll let her in, Claud." I ran downstairs, opened the door, warned Mary Anne about Janine, then ran back upstairs with Mary Anne at my heels. We ran straight to Claudia's room, careful not to look in at Janine as we ran by her open door.

"Hi," Claudia said, closing her door behind us. "You two, this is Stacey McGill. Stacey, this is Kristy Thomas and this is Mary Anne Spier."

"Hi!" Stacey and I said brightly.

Mary Anne suddenly turned shy. "Hi," she said softly, speaking more to a wall than to Stacey.

I looked at Stacey. I could see why she and Claudia were friends already. Stacey had on a pink sweat shirt with sequins and a large purple parrot on the front; short, tight-fitting jeans with zippers up the outsides of her legs; and pink plastic shoes. She was very pretty, tall and quite thin with huge blue eyes framed by dark lashes, and fluffy blonde hair that looked as if it had been permed recently. I glanced at Mary Anne. She and I were still in our school clothes—skirts and blouses. I was wearing white knee socks and loafers. Mary Anne was wearing short white socks and saddle shoes. Mary Anne's hair was, of course, in plaits, and I was wearing a blue hair band.

We looked like little schoolgirls. Stacey and Claudia looked like models.

There was an uncomfortable silence.

"Well," I cleared my throat. "Claudia, did you tell Stacey about the Babysitters Club?"

"Just what we talked about yesterday," she replied.

"Did you baby-sit in New York?" I asked Stacey.

"Oh, all the time. We lived in this big building. There were over two hundred flats in it—"

"Wow," said Mary Anne.

"—and I used to put up signs in the laundry room. People called me all the time." She paused. "I can stay out until ten on Friday and Saturday nights."

Another "Wow" from Mary Anne.

I was feeling more and more like a baby. How was it possible to feel so much younger than someone who was the same age as you?

"I'd really like to be in the club," said Stacey. "I don't know very many kids in Stoneybrook yet. And it'd be nice to earn some money. My mum and dad buy my clothes, but I have to earn money for other things—you know, tapes and jewellery and stuff."

"How come you left New York?" asked Mary Anne. Mary Anne has a real thing for New York—for glamour and lights and shops. She wants to live in the city after she's grown-up.

Stacey looked at the floor. She started jiggling her right foot back and forth. "Oh," she said lightly, "my dad changed his job. Gosh, you have a lot of super posters, Claudia."

"Thanks. I made those two myself." Claudia pointed to a picture of a horse galloping through a desert, and to another of a girl sitting on a window seat, gazing outside.

"Boy, if I lived in New York I wouldn't leave for anything," Mary Anne went on. "Tell me what it's like to live there. What was your school like?"

"Well," began Stacey, "I went to a private school."

"Did you have to wear a uniform?" asked Claudia, shuddering.

"Nope. We could wear normal clothes."

"How did you get to school?" asked Mary Anne.

"On the subway."

"Wow."

"Once," Stacey added, seeing how impressed Mary Anne was, "I took the subway all the way from our flat to Coney Island. I had to change about a zillion times."

"Wow. Did you ever take a cab by yourself?"

"Sure. Lots of times."

"Wow."

At Mary Anne's last "Wow" we all began giggling.

"Well, anyway," I said, "to get back to the Babysitters Club, what I think we should do is make two lists: one of rules, and one of things to do—"

"Does this mean," Stacey interrupted me, "that I'm in the club?"

I glanced at Mary Anne, who nodded her head. I already knew what Claudia thought.

"Yup," I said.

"Oh, hey! Great!" Stacey exclaimed, grinning.

Claudia gave her the thumbs-up sign. Then she pulled a packet of peanut crunch from under her pillow. "We should celebrate," she said, handing it round.

Mary Anne and I were starving and each gobbled down a handful, but Stacey just glanced at the packet and then passed it back to Claudia. "These are—you've only got five left," she said.

"Oh, go ahead," replied Claudia. "I've got lots of stuff stashed away. Mum and Dad don't know about it." She said she had bubble gum in her underwear drawer, a chocolate bar behind her encyclopaedias, a packet of Smarties in her desk drawer, and some peppermints in her piggy bank.

"No, thanks," said Stacey. "I'm, um, on a diet."

"You?" I cried. "You're skinny already!" Stacey was the first person my age I knew who was on a diet. "How much do you weigh?" I demanded.

"Kristy!" Claudia exclaimed. "That's none of your business."

"But it's not safe to diet if you don't need to. My mum said. Does your mother know you're dieting?"

"Well, she—"

"See, I'll bet she doesn't."

At that moment, someone knocked on Claudia's door. "Mary Anne!" Janine called. "Your father phoned on the other line. He says it's time for you to go home."

Mary Anne looked at her watch. "Six-ten!" she cried. "Oh, no, I'm late. Dad hates it when I'm late. Thanks, Janine. I have to go."

"Wait," I said. "We didn't finish making our plans."

"Let's meet tomorrow at break," suggested Claudia.

"Really?" I said. Recently, Claudia has been spending break watching the cute boys play basketball. She never wants to play games with Mary Anne and me.

"Sure," she said. "As soon as we've finished lunch we'll meet outside by the gym door. Somebody remember to bring a pad of paper and a pen."

"I will," I volunteered.

Mary Anne stood up then and practically flew home.

"I'd better go, too," said Stacey.

"Me, too," I said.

Claudia walked us to the door and we went our separate ways.

The Friday lunch at Stoneybrook Middle School is always the same: mince, cold lumpy mashed potatoes, a dinky cup of coleslaw, milk, and an ice cream.

I truly hate it, except for the ice cream.

After Mary Anne and I had forced down as much as possible, we went outside to wait for Claudia and Stacey. We hadn't sat with them in the cafeteria because they were eating at a table full of the most sophisticated girls in the class (whom we hardly knew) *and* some boys. How they could eat with boys was beyond me. The boys are always doing awful things like mashing up peas and ravioli in their milk cartons to see what colours they can make. Claudia seems to think those things are hilarious.

So Mary Anne and I reached the gym door first. We played a fast skipping game while we waited. I won. I usually do. I'm good at sports.

"Hi, you guys!" called Claudia about ten minutes later. She and Stacey were walking across the playground.

"Hi!" we answered.

The four of us went to a quiet corner of the school building and sat down on some empty packing crates.

"I've got the paper and pen," I said. "And something else." I pulled the list that I had made on Tuesday night from my pocket and pointed to section two, which was labelled ADVERTISING. "This is what we have to do next: Let people know what we're doing."

"Right," agreed Claudia from underneath an outrageous red felt hat, which her teacher wouldn't allow her to wear in the classroom.

"I think fliers are the easiest way to tell people about our club. We can make up a nice ad and my mum can xerox it at her office. Then we can stick copies in people's letterboxes. We can do it in our neighbourhood and in other streets, too. Anywhere that's in bike-riding distance. Mary Anne, your dad would let you sit in another neighbourhood if it weren't *too* far away, wouldn't he?"

"I guess so," Mary Anne replied uncertainly.

I saw Stacey glance curiously at Mary Anne.

"Good," I said. "Now, we already have a name—the Babysitters Club. Do you think we should have some kind of symbol or sign, too? You know, like the symbol that's on Girl Guide biscuits, or the sun that's on the stationery my mum's company uses?"

"Yeah!" said Stacey. "That's a good idea. We could put it on top of our fliers. Claudia, you could draw something for us."

"I don't know," said Claudia.

"Come on, you're a great artist," I exclaimed. "You can draw anything."

"I know I can draw, but I'm not good at . . . at symbols and stuff. Janine's better at those things."

"Oh, forget Janine," I said. "Anyway, we're all going to think of the symbol. We're a club. We have to agree on things. Now, what could we use?"

"Well," said Mary Anne, "it could either be something that has to do with baby-sitters, like a child or a helping hand, or it could just be something we like: a rainbow or a shooting star or a frog—"

"A frog!" I burst out. I began to giggle. So did Claudia and Stacey.

Mary Anne looked embarrassed. Then she began to laugh, too.

"How about a warthog?" suggested Claudia.

"A nerd!" said Stacey.

"Dog food!" We were all laughing so hard we could barely talk.

"Okay, let's be serious," I said when we had calmed down. "Lunch is going to be over in ten minutes."

"How about something with our names in it?" suggested Stacey.

"Yeah!" said Mary Anne and Claudia and I, but then we couldn't think of anything.

"How about a roof shape with our initials on it?" said Mary Anne.

"Wait a minute!" Claudia cried. "I've got it. I could draw something like this." She took the pen and paper from me and drew this:

"That's terrific! Really terrific!" I exclaimed. "It's perfect! Claudia, you're a—" I stopped. I'd almost said genius, but Claudia's pretty touchy about that word. "—a pro," I finished.

The bell rang then and we had to go inside. But first we agreed to spend the weekend working on the Babysitters Club.

5th CHAPTER

On Saturday the four members of the Babysitters Club worked very hard. Mary Anne and Claudia and I called all the families we already baby-sat for and told them about the club. Then we wrote a little ad about the club and phoned it in to the *Stoneybrook News*. It would appear on Wednesday. We couldn't wait to see it.

Then Stacey had an idea. "I think we should elect, you know, officers of the club." We were sitting around in Claudia's room as usual.

"Officers?" Claudia repeated, looking confused. She was probably thinking of policemen.

"Yeah. A chairman, a vice-chairman, a secretary, and . . . and . . ."

"A treasurer!" I supplied. "Perfect. Four officers, four of us."

"Oh, I get it," said Claudia. "Well, I

nominate Kristy for chairman. The club was her idea."

"I second it," said Mary Anne.

"Me, too," said Stacey. "It's unanimous."

I grinned. "Wow! Thanks, you guys. Okay, I nominate Claudia for vice-chairman since we're using her room and her phone and phone number. She may get a lot of calls to deal with when the rest of us aren't here."

"I second it," said Mary Anne.

"Me, too," chimed in Stacey. "Unanimous again."

Claudia beamed.

Mary Anne cleared her throat and looked around nervously. "Stacey, if you don't mind, I'd like to be secretary. I'm good at writing things down."

"That's perfect," said Stacey, "because I'm good with money and numbers. I was hoping I could be treasurer."

We didn't even bother to vote on Mary Anne and Stacey since everything was working out so well.

In celebration of the new officers, Claudia took a bag of wine gums out of her pencil case and passed it round.

Before the bag even reached Stacey, she leaped up, clapped her hands over her mouth, and exclaimed, "Oh, no! I have to go home, but I'll be right back."

"Stacey," I said, "if you're still on that dumb diet, you can just say so. You don't have to run away. Look, we'll put the wine gums back."

"No, no, it's not that. I just—I just forgot something. It'll only take a minute." Stacey dashed out of Claudia's room.

Mary Anne and Claudia and I looked at each other and shrugged.

Stacey returned about twenty minutes later. Her hands were empty.

"Where is it?" I asked her.

"Where's what?"

"What you forgot."

"What I . . . ? Oh, no, I just forgot to *do* something. But it's all taken care of."

I started to ask her another question, but Claudia flashed me a look that said I was being a pest.

We worked on our flier then, and when it was finished, this is what it looked like:

Need a baby-sitter?
Save time! Call:

THE BABYSITTERS CLUB
KL 5-3231

Monday, Wednesday, Friday 5.30–6.00
and reach four experienced baby-sitters.

Kristy Thomas, Chairman
Claudia Kishi, Vice-Chairman
Mary Anne Spier, Secretary
Stacey McGill, Treasurer

Available:
weekends
after school
evenings

Or call us one at a time, any time:

Kristy Thomas	KL 5-4378
Claudia Kishi	KL 5-3231
Mary Anne Spier	KL 5-9102
Stacey McGill	KL 5-7844

"I'll give the flier to my mum," I said. "She can xerox it on Monday and we can pass round the fliers next week. I've got to go home anyway. It's almost dinner time, and Mum's going out with Watson tonight." I made a face.

"Who's Watson?" asked Stacey.

"Her boyfriend," I replied. "My parents are divorced."

"Oh," said Stacey, looking slightly uncomfortable.

"Are your parents divorced, too?" I asked. I realized how little I knew about her.

"Nope. They've been married for fifteen years."

"Mine have been married for twenty years," said Claudia.

"My mother died when I was a baby," said Mary Anne quietly. "She had cancer."

Again Stacey looked embarrassed.

"It's all right. Really. I don't remember her. But sometimes I wish I did."

I stood up. "Well, I'd really better go. See you tomorrow," I called as I started down the Kishis' stairs.

Watson arrived at 6.30.

David Michael ran to meet him. He loves Watson. That's because he doesn't remember Dad, so he thinks Watson is better than no father at all.

I stayed in my room until Mum yelled up to me, "Kristy! Watson's here!"

48

Why does she always make me come down to see Watson? She knows how I feel about him.

"Coming," I said, trying to sound put-out, as if she had interrupted something important.

When I came downstairs, Watson was standing in the kitchen with cartons of Chinese food. "Surprise!" he said.

"What?" I asked suspiciously.

"Isn't this nice, Kristy?" said Mum brightly. "Watson brought over Chinese food so we can all eat together before he and I go out."

Watson's always bringing over food. You'd think he owned a restaurant.

"Who's taking care of your kids?" I asked pointedly. I thought it was really stinky that on the weekend his kids came to stay, Watson not only had to go to work, but left the kids with a baby-sitter while he went out with my mother.

"I found a very nice baby-sitter," Watson replied pleasantly. "She took care of Andrew and Karen this morning while I went to the office, and they liked her very much."

"Oh," I said.

Watson set the white cartons on the table and began opening them while Sam and I got our plates, napkins, and cutlery. I made a face at Sam to show him what I thought about the dinner, but Sam said, "Thanks, Watson. This is really great." Sam and

Charlie sort of like Watson, too. Once Sam even baby-sat for Watson's kids. I, for one, will never, every baby-sit for them. I bet they're brats.

"Yeah," said Charlie. "I'm taking Carole out for hamburgers tonight, but I don't mind eating first." Charlie has a stomach like a trash compacter.

"Mum?" I asked. "Is there any of that leftover chilli?"

Mum glared at me. She didn't answer my question.

"What's wrong, Kristy?" said Watson. "I thought you liked Chinese food."

"It's okay, I guess. But I don't feel like it tonight."

Watson looked slightly hurt.

When the table was set, we sat down and everyone began helping themselves to Moo Shoo pork and chicken with cashews and beef with *mange tout* and the other things Watson had brought. I was starving, and I *love* Chinese food, especially chicken with cashews, but I wouldn't let Watson know. Since there was no chilli, I made myself a peanut butter and strawberry jam sandwich. I slapped it on my plate and then began nibbling it into the shape of a snowman. I was just about to bite off the snowman's head when Watson said, "So, how are things, Kristy?"

"Fine."

"School okay?"

"Yup."

"What are you doing that's new or interesting?"

"Nothing."

"Hey, Watson, the Maths Club won its third maths meet yesterday," Sam said, coming to the rescue. He hates it when I bug Watson.

Watson needed a second to collect himself. He doesn't understand me. "What, Sam? . . . Oh, your *third* meet? That's great!"

"And guess what!" exclaimed David Michael. "Mum's going to get me a new G.I. Joe—one of the good guys."

"That sounds pretty exciting," said Watson. "I don't know much about G.I. Joe dolls, though. I don't think Andrew plays with them."

"Oh, he probably does," I said airily, "and you just don't know it because you're not around enough. All the boys play with them." I glanced at Mum. I could practically see smoke coming from her ears as she let me know that I was getting into *trouble*, but I went on anyway. "Besides, they're action toys, not dolls. Right, David Michael?"

David Michael beamed. "Right, Kristy."

"And Karen probably has a Rainbow Brite doll. Ever heard of those?"

At that moment, Mum slammed her fork onto her plate. She stood up so fast she almost tipped her chair over. "Kristy, apologize to Watson this instant, and then go to your room."

"But," I said politely, "I haven't finished this delicious dinner yet."

"Kristin Amanda Thomas! You are *asking* for it, young lady!"

I got to my feet. "I'm sorry, Watson," I mumbled. I walked out of the kitchen and started up the stairs. When I was halfway up, I yelled over my shoulder, "I'm sorry you're such a terrible father!" Then I ran to my room and slammed the door.

See, the thing is, Watson is actually a very good father. Karen and Andrew and their mother live right here in Stoneybrook, and Watson has the kids at his house each time he's supposed to. Plus, he celebrates every other holiday with them, and never forgets the ones in between. (My dad forgets holidays all the time.) But I still don't like Watson horning in on our family. He doesn't belong with us.

Mum and Watson left without saying goodbye to me.

I felt really guilty about what I'd done.

Before I went to sleep I left a note on Mum's bed. It said: *Dear Mum, I'm sorry I was so rude. I guess I haven't learned much about decorum yet. I hope you had fun on your date. I love you. Kristy.*

When I woke up the next morning, I found a note to me from Mum. It said: *Dear Kristy, I love you, too. Mum.*

6th CHAPTER

On Wednesday afternoon, I raced home from school and made a frantic search of the front garden for our copy of the *Stoneybrook News*. I found it under a peony bush in the garden. I threw my things on the ground, sat down right in the middle of the lawn, and leafed through the paper until I found the advertising section. And sure enough, the fifth ad from the bottom in the third column was ours. This is what it looked like:

THE BABYSITTERS CLUB

Need a baby-sitter?
Make one call, reach four sitters,
Call KL 5-3231 Mon., Wed.,
Fri., 5.30-6.00

We had wanted to include more information in the ad, like the other phone numbers, but when we called the newspaper, we found out they charged you per *line* to run an ad. Our little ad was already pretty expensive, and we'd had to use our entire first week's club subs to pay for it. Still, the ad was awfully exciting. It was fun being in the newspaper.

"Hey, Kristy, what are you doing?" Claudia came running across our lawn, her knapsack bouncing against her back.

"Look!" I exclaimed. "Here it is! Our ad!"

"Ooh, let me see!"

Claudia dropped to her knees beside me, and I jabbed at the ad.

"Wow! Now if we can just finish handing round those fliers today," she said, "we might actually get some calls on Friday."

"I know!" I felt like squealing and jumping up and down.

"Let's get Mary Anne to help us."

"Okay," I said. "And Stacey."

"No, she's busy this afternoon. She told me so in school today."

"What's she doing?"

"Don't know. Come on. Are you ready?"

"Let me just put my books inside," I said, "and see if Kathy's got here yet. She's baby-sitting for David Michael today."

Kathy and David Michael were playing snakes and ladders on the back porch, so I grabbed the last of the fliers from my desk and ran outside to Claudia. "My mum xeroxed five more yesterday. That's all I have left," I said.

"I've got six more."

We found Mary Anne, who also had six left, and we took off on our bicycles for Quentin Court, which is a few streets away from Stacey's house. There we put the last of the fliers in letter-boxes.

"Done!" I said to Claudia and Mary Anne.

They grinned at me.

"Now I guess we just sit back and wait for calls."

"Right."

"Right."

Two days later, the members of the Babysitters Club gathered eagerly in Claudia's bedroom. Even though the fliers said for clients to call us between 5.30 and 6.00, we all managed to show up early. I was the first person there. I knocked on Claudia's bedroom door, which now had an official-looking sign on it reading:

THE BABYSITTERS CLUB
Hours: Mon., Wed., Fri. 5.30—6.00

"Come in!" called Claudia. It was only 4.30 when I entered her room, but I found her sitting cross-legged on the bed with the phone in her lap, one hand clutching the receiver.

"The phone's not going to run away, you

know," I greeted her.

Claudia grinned sheepishly. "I know. I'm just so excited."

Actually, I was, too. "So am I!" I squealed, suddenly. I dashed across the room and jumped on her bed. "I've been waiting all week for today to come. What do you think will happen? Oh, this has just got to work. I know we'll have some customers. We'll have customers, won't we?" I grabbed the phone from Claudia and held it in *my* lap.

It was 5.05 when Stacey and Mary Anne arrived.

The four of us sat on Claudia's bed.

Nobody said a word.

At 5.10, Claudia got up, took a shoe box labelled SNEAKERS out of her cupboard, opened it, and handed around some toffee. As usual, Stacey refused.

At 5.25, I began staring at my watch, following the minute hand round and round—5.26, 5.27, 5.28, 5.29.

At exactly 5.30 the phone rang.

I screamed.

"Oh, no! I don't believe it!" cried Mary Anne.

Claudia spat out her toffee. "I'll answer it, I'll answer it," she shrieked. She jerked up the receiver and said politely, "Good afternoon. Babysitters Club."

Then she made a face and handed me the phone. "Kristy, it's your mother."

I spat out my toffee, too. "*Mm-um!*" I exclaimed as soon as I got on the phone. "These are our business hours. You're not supposed to—What? You do? Oh." I calmed down. "Please hold on for a moment."

I put my hand over the receiver. "Mum needs a sitter for David Michael!" I cried. "Kathy can't come next Wednesday."

Everyone suppressed shrieks.

"I've got our appointment book right here," said Claudia. "Now let's see. Mary Anne, you have to go to the dentist that day, and I have art class. That leaves you"— Claudia pointed to me—"and Stacey."

What should we do? "Just another sec, Mum," I said.

I hadn't really thought about what to do if several of us were available for the same job.

"Well . . ." I began.

"He's your brother," Stacey said. "You should get the job."

"But if you took it, you'd get to know some other people in the neighbourhood. You'd probably meet Sam and Charlie— they're my big brothers."

"Brothers?" Stacey's eyes lit up. Boys! "But what are you going to do while I baby-sit? Hang round and watch?"

"Well, I *hope* I'll have another job," I said huffily. "You take the job, Stacey. I don't want my first Babysitters Club client to be my own mother."

"Okay, if you're sure," Stacey said slowly. Then she grinned. "Thanks!"

"No problem," I said. I took my hand off the receiver. "Mum, Stacey will baby-sit for David Michael on Wednesday. The usual time, right? . . . Okay. Hey, where are you calling from anyway? . . . Oh, the office."

Claudia elbowed me. "Quit tying up the line. Someone else might be trying to get through."

I nodded. "Mum, I have to get off. I'll see you in a little while . . . Okay . . . Okay . . . Bye." I hung up.

The phone rang again immediately. Claudia gave me a look that said, I told you so.

"Can I answer it?" Mary Anne asked.

"Sure," I said.

Mary Anne picked up the phone. "Good afternoon. Babysitters Club," she said. There was a long pause. "I think you have the wrong number. There's no Jim Bartolini here." She hung up.

At 5.42 the phone rang for a third time. We all looked at each other. "You get it, Kristy," Mary Anne said. "You're the chairman."

"Okay . . . Hello. Babysitters Club . . . Yes . . . yes. Just a moment, please." I put my hand over the mouthpiece. "Do any of you know a Mrs McKeever? She lives on Quentin Court."

The girls shook their heads.

"What's she got?" asked Claudia.

"Two kids, Buffy and Pinky," I replied.

"Buffy and Pinky!" cried Stacey. "*Buffy* and *Pinky*?"

"*Shh*," I warned her.

"How old are they?" Mary Anne wanted to know.

"I don't know. Hold on . . . Hello, Mrs McKeever? We need a little information, please. How old are Buffy and Pinky? . . . *Oh*. Okay." I turned back to the members of my club. "She says they're three. They must be twins."

"When does she need a sitter?" asked Mary Anne.

"Wednesday afternoon. Oh, I guess I'm the only one who's free then," I suddenly realized. I was dying for a new client anyway. I accepted the job and took down the information I needed. Then Mrs McKeever asked me a zillion questions about myself. She wanted to know how old I was and how much experience I had and that sort of thing.

When I hung up the phone, I said to Mary Anne, "Hey, secretary, you've got to record these jobs in the appointment book."

"Oh, right." I handed her the book and she got right to work.

The next two calls were for Jim Bartolini.

Claudia was growing exasperated. "Boy, this is *weird*," she said. "I've got wrong numbers before, but no one's ever asked for Jim Bartolini. Certainly not three no ones."

At 5.55 Mary Anne stood up. "I'd better get going," she said. She pulled on her sweater and slurped loudly on the remaining bit of her toffee.

The phone rang. Stacey answered it and handed it to me. "It's your mum again, Kristy."

I rolled my eyes, "Mum?" I said. "Did Kathy back out of her other afternoon, too? . . . Oh . . . *Oh* . . . *Oh* . . no. Not *me*. I am *not* baby-sitting for them. You know how I feel. Okay, but hold on . . . Watson needs a baby-sitter for his kids again on Saturday morning. Not tomorrow, but next Saturday," I told the others. "*I'm* not doing it."

"I'll do it," Mary Anne said. "I'm getting curious about them. Aren't you curious, Kristy?"

I was *dying* to see what kind of monsters Watson had. "Not really," I said. "Sign yourself up for the job."

As Mary Anne was about to walk out of Claudia's room, the phone rang for the seventh time since 5.30. "I'll get it," said Mary Anne. "One last call . . . Hello? . . . *What?* Mary Anne's plaits practically stood on end. "It's some boy on the phone," she told us. "He says his name is Jim Bartolini. He wants to know if there have been any calls for him!"

"You're kidding!" exclaimed Claudia.

"Oh, *wait* a second!" I said suddenly. I grabbed the phone from Mary Anne. "Sam, is that you?"

"No," said the voice on the other end of the phone. "It's Jim Bartolini. I was wondering if—"

"Sam, you're a rat!" I cried. "This is important business. And furthermore, I'm telling!" I slammed the receiver down.

"The nerve!" said Mary Anne.

But Claudia and Stacey began giggling. "I think that was sort of funny," said Claudia.

"You would," I retorted.

"Oh, come on. You have to admit that was a pretty good goof call. It's better than just 'Is your refrigerator running?' or something."

"I guess," I said.

So the first Babysitters Club office hour (or office half hour) ended on a sour note. And the evening didn't improve much. I went home and did tell Mum what Sam had done, and Sam called me a rat, and I said, "I know you are, but what am I?" and Sam said, "I know you are, but what am I?" and I shouted, "You're driving me crazy!" and Sam shouted, "You're driving me crazy!" and Mum told Sam he couldn't use the phone for an hour and sent me to my room, which suited me fine since Watson was on his way over.

Shortly before Mum and Watson left on another date, I was allowed to leave my room to take a phone call. It was Claudia. "I've just got a job!" she said. "Mrs Newton called. She needed a sitter for tomorrow, so I took the job."

Mrs Newton? "That's great, Claud," I said, but I hung up the phone feeling pretty low. *I* usually sit for Jamie. Claudia should have told the other club members when a job was offered, not just taken it herself. Just because the main phone number was hers didn't mean she got first crack at every job that came along. And how come Mrs Newton had called *that* number after six when she was probably trying to reach me? I guessed people didn't pay much attention to hours and phone numbers, which was a shame considering all the trouble we'd gone to with our fliers and the newspaper ad. I flashed the news to Mary Anne at nine o'clock, and she flashed back TOO BAD.

Well, I thought, as I went to bed that night with Louie curled at my feet, at least I've got a new client. On Wednesday I'll get to meet Pinky and Buffy McKeever. New clients are always interesting.

If only I'd had some idea just how interesting they were going to be.

7th CHAPTER

On Wednesday afternoon, I was all set for my first job for the Babysitters Club. I couldn't wait to meet Pinky and Buffy. I'd never sat for twins before. I wondered what it would be like. Would they play tricks on me? And what could Pinky and Buffy be nicknames for? I'd find out soon enough.

I walked over to Quentin Court right after I got home from school. I left a little early, just in case I had any trouble finding the McKeevers' house. Mrs McKeever had said the address was 52 Quentin Court. So I found the side of the street with the even-numbered addresses on it and started walking. There was 22 Quentin Court, 28 Quentin Court, 34, 40, 46, and sure enough there was number 52.

I stood and looked at the house for a moment. It was a perfectly nice house, painted white with neat black shutters. But

63

something was wrong. What was it? After a moment it came to me.

There were no signs of children.

There were no toys in the garden or tricycles in the drive, no sneakers on the front step or artwork in the windows. I hoped Pinky and Buffy weren't going to be boring children who wanted to spend the afternoon learning about butterflies or food groups or something.

My enthusiasm was beginning to wane just a little, but I took a deep breath and marched myself straight to the front door.

Ding-dong.

Silence. No running feet or shouts like I would hear when I rang the Newtons' bell.

After a few moments, the door was opened.

A plump, pleasant-looking young woman stood on the other side of the step, smiling. Well, I thought, at least Pinky and Buffy's mother doesn't look boring.

"Hello?" she said.

"Hi, I'm Kristy Thomas. I'm here to baby-sit for Pinky and Buffy, the twins."

There was a pause, and then the woman said, "Yes. Won't you come in?"

I stepped inside into a very pretty room. But again, something seemed wrong, and it took me a moment to work out what it was. Then I realized. Pinky and Buffy must have been not only very boring three-year-olds but very careful three-year-olds. The reason the room was so pretty was because it was full of glass and china—big Oriental vases, little glass statues, even plates that were displayed on delicate stands. Everything was breakable. In our house, what with David Michael and footballs and tennis balls and friends coming over all the time, breakable stuff is pratically against the law.

Then I saw that the area we were standing in—the foyer and the living room—was blocked off with baby gates. That explained the china, but it didn't seem to be very nice for Pinky and Buffy.

It also occurred to me that I couldn't hear any children's voices or giggling. Suddenly I began to feel suspicious. What had I got myself into? The McKeevers were strangers to me. Maybe I'd been lured into—No, that was silly. At breakfast that morning, when I'd told my mother where I would be after school, she'd just raised an eyebrow. She hadn't said, Don't go, Kristy. We'll never see you again!

I smiled brightly at the woman. "So," I said. "Where are Pinky and Buffy?"

"Oh, they're in the laundry room," she replied.

The laundry room? Were they being punished? I'd got angry with David Michael a few times, but I'd *never* stuck him in the laundry room.

"Let me introduce myself," the woman went on. "I am Miss Hargreaves, Mrs

McKeever's niece. Mrs McKeever is away for several days, which is why we need help with Pinky and Buffy. I have an important appointment this afternoon, and we find that we need someone with Pinky and Buffy at all times."

Well, if they were only three, what was she expecting?

"They're a bit unruly," Miss Hargreaves added.

"Ohhh," I said knowingly, wondering where the signs of unruliness were in the quiet house. "Well, that's okay. I know all about 'unruly'. I've got three brothers."

"Have you?"

I nodded. "Well, let's go and get them out of the laundry room. They're probably ready to play. Maybe we could all take a walk to the brook."

"That would be lovely," replied Miss Hargreaves, "but it might be difficult for you to manage."

"Oh, I've had lots of experience."

"That's fine, then."

"Are Pinky and Buffy boys or girls?" I asked.

"Well, it doesn't much matter, of course—" It *doesn't*?

"—but Buffy's a boy and Pinky's a girl."

"Oh, that's easy to remember," I said. I was trying to sound pleasant, but already I had a very bad case of the creeps.

"Here we are!" Miss Hargreaves

announced. We were standing by a door next to the kitchen. "Now get ready. These two monsters of my aunt's will practically break the door down," she said affectionately.

My eyes opened wide. "They will?"

"Stand back."

I stood back. I wished I could stand all the way back at my house.

Miss Hargreaves opened the door. Two huge, fluffy, drooling, barking Saint Bernards hurled themselves into the hall, almost knocking each other and Miss Hargreaves over.

I shrieked. "Do I have to take care of them too?"

"Too?" repeated Miss Hargreaves. "Who else is going to help you?"

"No, I mean, do I have to watch them *plus* Pinky and Buffy?"

"Oh, my dear! Those *are* Pinky and Buffy!"

"But—but—"I sputtered, "I'm a *baby*-sitter, not a *dog*-sitter!"

Miss Hargreaves looked confused. "I don't know what arrangements my aunt made," she said at last, "but here are the dogs, and here *you* are, and I have to leave."

"But—but—"

"Oh, it's not *so* difficult," she went on. "They need to be outside as much as possible. Our garden isn't fenced in, so you may either take them out on their leads, or stay with them in the back garden. If you play with them, they won't run away. Now, their footballs are in the box by the back door, their leads are hanging on the peg above, and at four-thirty they need their food—a tin apiece—and they can each have one biscuit as a treat. The emergency numbers are posted by the phone in the kitchen, just in case. Do you have any questions?"

I shook my head dazedly.

Buffy and Pinky leaped around, galumphing after Miss Hargreaves as she put on her coat and went out to meet the cab that had come to pick her up.

Shaking, I let the dogs out in the back garden, remembering to bring their footballs. I tossed a red football gingerly towards them as they ran ahead of me. I wasn't sure what they'd do with it. Louie usually runs half-heartedly after a football and then sort of forgets to fetch it.

Not these two. They dived for the ball, crashing into each other. One of them got it away from the other, but I couldn't tell which one. They looked identical.

I got down on my knees and clapped my hands. "Okay, boy, bring it here!" I called, not caring whether the dog was Pinky or Buffy.

Whichever one it was came barrelling straight towards me. I knew that game all right. Louie likes it, too. He runs for you, then turns at the last second and veers round you. You can almost see him grinning.

But not this dog. He ran right over me. I was lost in a whirl of fur and claws and playful woofs. You really haven't lived until a dog has stepped on your face.

I sat up and rubbed my cheeks and eyes. Nothing seemed to be bleeding, so I stood up shakily. I looked round.

Oh, no. The dogs were gone! I thought Miss Hargreaves had said they would stay in the garden with me. Maybe they didn't stay with people they'd practically knocked unconscious.

"Pinky!" I shouted. "Buffy!"

Nothing.

"Pink-*ee!* Buff-*ee!*"

I ran to the front of the house. No dogs. I looked up and down the street. No dogs.

I ran to the back garden and looked again. And there they were. Not in the McKeevers' yard, but in the garden next door. They were racing toward me—heading for a clothes-line.

"Pinky, Buffy, *no!*"

Too late. They streaked through all the clothes and came to a screeching halt about two feet from me. One was wearing a small blanket draped over his (her?) tail. The other had a slip in his mouth.

"Bad dogs!" I cried. "Sit . . . *Sit!*"

I took the blanket and the slip from them and glanced nervously at the house next door. It seemed pretty quiet. Maybe no one was home. Thank goodness the clothes-line seemed okay except for the missing blanket and slip.

I wanted to return the things, but what about Pinky and Buffy? If I went into the other garden, would they follow me? Would they run away? I didn't know what to do. I almost didn't care. But just then a car pulled into the drive of the house. Luckily, the drive was on the other side of the house from where I was, but I knew I'd better do something fast. Someone could come out at any moment to bring in the laundry.

"Okay, you guys," I said to the dogs. "Look, here are your footballs." I began walking slowly backwards, towards the clothes-line. The dogs crept after me as if they were stalking the balls.

I reached the clothes-line. The dogs were still following me.

"Come on," I whispered tantalizingly. I held the balls under one arm, pinned the blanket and the slip crookedly to the line, and raced back to the McKeevers' garden at top speed.

The dogs ran after me. They liked that game.

Good for them. They could follow me all the way into the house, which was just what they did, and just where I wanted them.

We stayed inside for the rest of the afternoon, since I didn't trust the dogs outdoors any more, even on their leads. I watched TV. The dogs chewed on their footballs. Any time they started to get rowdy, I just held open the door to the laundry room and they calmed down. By the time Miss Hargreaves returned, I had decided something important. The members of the Babysitters Club should keep a notebook. Each time one of us finished a job, we should write it up in the notebook and the others should read about it. That way we could learn about each other's experiences. With a little luck, we wouldn't make any mistake more than once. For instance, no more dog-sitting.

I ran home, eager to start the notebook.

My first Babysitters Club job was over. I had earned three dollars and fifty cents.

8th
CHAPTER

Thursday, September 25th

Kristy says we have to keep a record of every babysitting job we do in this book. My first job through the Baby-sitters Club was last Saturday. I was sitting for Jamie Newton only it wasn't just for Jamie it was for Jamie and his three cousins. Four kids altogether! Mrs. Newton didn't tell me that over the phone. Anyway, the kids were Jamie plus Rosie who was three, Brenda who was five and Rob who was eight. Ooh boy were they wild!

Claudia didn't have an easy time of it at the Newtons', that was for sure. She called me on Sunday to tell me all about it. I was almost glad I hadn't got the job. What happened was that Mrs Newton's sister, Mrs Feldman, and her husband and their three kids were visiting, and the adults had got invitations to a show at an art gallery or something, so Mrs Newton needed a baby-sitter for Jamie and his cousins. But somehow she forgot to mention that to Claudia, which wasn't at all like Mrs Newton. It must have been because she's pregnant and thinking about the baby. Ordinarily Mrs Newton is honest and thoughtful. She always calls her baby-sitters if there are any changes in plans. Once she even called when Jamie had come down with a cold, to ask whether I still wanted to come since I would risk catching it from him.

But things must have been slipping Mrs Newton's mind, because when Claudia showed up that Saturday, four children were waiting for her. And there were a whole lot of problems. Jamie and Rosie apparently didn't like each other, Brenda was cranky (*very* cranky) because she was getting over chickenpox, and Rob hated girls, which included Rosie, Brenda, Jamie's mother, his own mother, and girl baby-sitters.

When Claudia stepped into the living room, Rob was sulking on one end of the couch, muttering things like, "Stupid girls," and, "Why do we have to have a dumb *girl* baby-sit for us?" Brenda was crying and clutching Mrs Feldman round the legs, which made it hard for both of them to move, and Rosie and Jamie were fighting.

Rosie was trying to yank something out of Jamie's hand.

"That's mine!" Jamie yelled indignantly.

"It is not. It's mine!" Rosie made off with her prize and charged up the stairs.

Jamie ran after her. "It is not! It's mine!"

"*Mine!*"

"*Mine!!*" shouted Jamie at the top of his lungs. (Claudia said the house was practically shaking.) "Girls don't play with trucks. That's my moving van! Give it to me!"

"*Nonononononono!*"

Since the adults hadn't left yet, Claudia wasn't sure whether she was supposed to break up the fight or let one of the parents do it. Just as she was about to dash up the stairs, Mrs Feldman managed to unwrap Brenda from her legs and chase after Jamie and Rosie. She took each one by the hand and walked them downstairs, explaining patiently, "Jamie, sometimes girls *do* play with trucks. Rosie and Brenda do. But Rosie, you don't have a moving van like this one. You must have got confused. That belongs to Jamie—"

"*See*," said Jamie and stuck out his tongue. Rosie stuck hers out, too.

"—so we'll get your tipper truck out of the goody bag," continued Mrs Feldman. "You brought three trucks with you, remember? Now maybe you and Jamie can play together nicely."

Jamie and Rosie looked at each other suspiciously.

Brenda burst into tears again and grabbed hold of her mother. And that's just how things were by the time Jamie's parents and the Feldmans left, except that Brenda was hugging a ratty teddy bear instead of her mother's legs.

Claudia looked round the living room nervously.

Rob looked round in disgust. His eyes fell on Jamie, who turned his back on Rosie and was pushing an ambulance back and forth, making loud siren noises. "Hey, Jamie," said Rob, "let's get away from all these *girls*, okay?" He glanced defiantly at Claudia.

" 'kay," replied Jamie vaguely, busy with the ambulance.

"Where are you going?" asked Claudia.

"I'm not telling," said Rob, and grabbed Jamie by the wrist.

Claudia dashed across the living room and blocked the doorway. Rob pulled Jamie round and hauled him off in another direction, towards the entrance to the dining room. Claudia beat him to it.

"Where are you going?" she asked him again. "I'm the baby-sitter and I have to know. Just tell me where you're going."

"Who's going to make me?"

"Nobody. But I won't let you leave until you do."

Rob whirled round again. He let go of Jamie and grabbed his sister instead. Jamie sat down on the floor in surprise.

"Have we ever had a baby-sitter as mean as *her*?" Rob asked angrily.

"No!" said Rosie.

"No," sniffled Brenda, who hadn't quite finished crying.

"Are we going to let her be mean?"

"No?" shouted his sisters.

"Okay, let's do it!"

Claudia said that her stomach felt as if it were on a roller coaster. She had no idea what the Feldman kids were going to do. She found out immediately.

Rosie began running round and round the room yelling at the top of her lungs. She wasn't yelling words; she was just making a noise. Brenda leaped onto the Newtons' couch and jumped up and down on it as if it were a trampoline. And Rob turned his fingers into guns and aimed them at Claudia. "*Pow! Pow! Pow-pow-pow!* You're a dead man! ... I mean, a dead lady." Jamie looked on dazedly.

At that point, Claudia almost panicked and called Stacey for help, but Jamie, sitting quietly on the floor, inspired her. She remembered that when she was little, and she or Janine misbehaved, her mother used to turn to her father and murmur. "I-g-n-o-r-e." And they would do just that. Claudia decided to try it on the Feldmans. She sat on the floor next to Jamie, reached for a copy of *The Tale of Peter Rabbit* lying abandoned by an armchair, and began to read to him. Jamie rested his head against her shoulder.

Thump, thump, thump went Brenda.

"*Aiieeee!*" shrieked Rosie, running by Claudia and stepping on her lap. Claudia didn't even look up.

"*Pow!*" shouted Rob. "*Pow!* . . . Hey, baby-sitter, I'm killing you! . . . Okay? . . . Baby-sitter?"

"Not now," said Claudia. "I'm busy."

She kept reading, raising her voice when she got to the part where Mr McGregor chased after Peter, waving a rake.

The thumping stopped. Brenda sat down a few feet away from Claudia and tried to listen without appearing *too* interested.

Rosie continued to run round the room, but she stopped yelling, and every time she ran by Claudia she slowed down long enough to look at the pictures in the book.

By the time the story was over, Jamie, Rosie, and Brenda were as quiet as mice. Claudia moved them to the couch. She found a copy of *Where the Wild Things Are*, opened it, and read about Max putting on his wolf suit and making mischief.

"As much mischief as me?" asked Rob

from across the room, dropping his guns.

"Not quite," replied Claudia. Rob looked satisfied. "If you come over here," she went on, "you can find out what happened to him."

Rob didn't say anything, but he perched on the arm of the couch and listened to the story. And to two more after that.

And that was Claudia's first Babysitters Club job (and the story of how she tamed the Feldmans).

9th CHAPTER

Thursday, September 25

Yesterday I babysat for Kristy's little brother, David Michael. Kristy told us to write in the Baby-sitters Club Notebook so we could keep track of any problems we had with Baby-sitters Club jobs, but taking care of David Michael was no trouble at all. He was very good. While Kristy was chasing around after those two elephants, Punky and Miffy, or whatever their names are, I was having a fine time with David Michael.

Ha! Stacey had a fine time at my house, all right, but she had it discovering Sam.

Stacey is boy-crazy and my brother is girl-crazy. They were perfect for each other. Not that Stacey neglected David Michael. But she did talk an awful lot about Sam after Wednesday. And Sam talked a lot about Stacey. Now here's the interesting part. *Sam is in high school.* And Stacey is only twelve. Most high school boys wouldn't be caught dead with a lowly middle school girl—unless the girl was a knockout. So I guessed that Stacey's permed hair and colourful clothes (and the fact that she came from New York City) made her pretty special.

Anyway, Stacey got to my house just as David Michael was coming home from school, and about ten minutes before I dashed off to what turned out to be my dog-sitting job. I gave her a very fast introduction to our house (not knowing whether Sam or Charlie would be home soon).

"Here's-the-kitchen-the-dishwasher's-broken-David-Michael-can-have-a-snack-biscuits-in-the-tin-nothing-after-four-thirty-he's-allergic-to-chocolate-oh-here's-Louie-he-won't-be-any-trouble-at-all-the-phone-numbers-are-on-the-bulletin-board-Mum's-is-on-the-phone-you-know-where-I'll-be-the-TV's-in-the-playroom-we're-not-allowed-to-watch-videos-when-Mum's-not-home-David-Michael-likes-playing-snakes-and-ladders-it's-in-the-cabinet-by-the-stereo-see-if-there-are-any-notes-from-his-teacher-in-his-school-bag-any-questions?"

Stacey shook her head.

"Okay." I knelt in front of David Michael. "This is Stacey," I told him. "She's my friend. She's going to baby-sit for you today."

David Michael nodded. He's used to baby-sitters.

"I'm going to be baby-sitting somewhere else, not far away. I'll be back around five. Oh, Stacey, my big brothers are Charlie and Sam. Charlie is sixteen and Sam is fourteen. I don't know what they're doing this afternoon. They might be around, they might not. Have fun, you two!" I ran out of the front door.

Stacey said that she and David Michael sat down at the kitchen table to have a snack. I hadn't been gone for more than five minutes when Sam showed up. He seemed to be angry about something. He was slamming his fist into his other hand. But he stopped short when he saw Stacey sitting in the kitchen. According to Sam, Stacey was a cute girl. According to Stacey, Sam was a gorgeous hunk. When I heard that later, I thought about what they looked like, and tried to work out what they saw in each other. (I have *absolutely no interest* in boys, of course. Still, I realized that that kind of information might be useful some day.)

I remembered that Stacey was wearing a matching top and skirt made of grey sweat shirt material with big yellow number tens all over it. Her hair was pinned back with clips shaped like rainbows. Little silver whistles were dangling from her ears. It was all very cool, but it seemed kind of young-looking. And she was drinking a glass of milk.

I thought about Sam. Now, he *is* pretty good-looking, with dark curly hair and sparkly blue eyes and a few freckles, but he was wearing jeans so ratty he'd once promised Mum he'd throw them away (but then hadn't been able to go through with it), a T-shirt that said: I KNOW YOU ARE, BUT WHAT AM I? To top if off, he was mad.

So where did the cute girl and the gorgeous hunk come from? Was it the perm? The freckles?

I couldn't work it out.

Anyway, Sam stopped being mad and Stacey finished the milk she was drinking as fast as she could, and checked to be sure she didn't have any on her upper lip.

"Hi," said Stacey.

"Hel-*lo*," said Sam. He put his books on the table, leaned against the counter, and crossed his legs, running his fingers through his hair. I've seen him do that. He thinks it makes him look cool and casual.

Stacey and Sam both spoke at once.

"I'm Stacey, Kristy's friend," said

82

Stacey, just as Sam said, "You must be Stacey."

"Oh," said Stacey, flattered. "Has Kristy mentioned me?"

"Uh, yeah. Well, she said you were going to baby-sit today. I was going to go over to this boy Ernest's house, but maybe . . . but I think he's busy or something. So I'll just stick around here."

"Well, listen," replied Stacey, "do you want me to leave? There's no reason for your mum to pay me to baby-sit if you're going to be at home."

"No, no," said Sam quickly. "The deal with my mum is that Charlie and Kristy and I only have to baby-sit David Michael one day a week each. The rest of the time we can do whatever we want, even if we're at home."

"Wow, that's really nice of your mum."

"Can I have a biscuit?" David Michael interrupted them.

Stacey looked at her watch. "I guess so. Do you think you'll still be able to eat your dinner tonight?"

"Yes," replied David Michael firmly.

"Okay."

David Michael got a packet of biscuits from the cupboard, opened it, took one out, and handed another to Sam. "Here," he said. "You want it?"

"Sure." Sam took the biscuit, broke it in half, and gave one piece to Stacey.

"Oh . . . no, thanks," she said.

"You must be the one on the diet," Sam said. "Kristy told me one of her friends was dieting. That sure takes willpower."

"I guess." Stacey stood up. "So," she said to David Michael. "How about some snakes-and-ladders?"

"Yeah!"

"Hey, I'll play too," said Sam. "We can have a championship series. First one to win two games is the snakes-and-ladders Champion of the Universe."

"*You're* going to play?" David Michael's eyes widened.

"Yeah, sure."

"But you nev—"

"Hey, little brother, your shoe's untied."

"It is?" David Michael looked at his feet. He was wearing sneakers that fastened with Velcro straps. "I don't *have* laces," he said witheringly.

"Made you look!" Sam ran out of the kitchen.

"You—you—I'm telling!" cried David Michael.

"Hey, squirt!" Sam called from the playroom. "Come on! We'd better start playing if we're going to have time for a championship series."

So David Michael, Stacey, and Sam settled themselves on the floor and played snakes-and-ladders. They were still playing when I got home from dog-sitting. Later, in the privacy of my room, Stacey said they'd had a great time except that Sam kept teasing David Michael and accusing him of cheating. Stacey didn't know whether to laugh with Sam since she wanted to impress him, or take David Michael's side since she was his baby-sitter. She said she did both. Then I told Stacey about Pinky and Buffy McKeever, and Stacey laughed until she was practically hysterical.

All things considered, Stacey definitely had the easiest of the first four Babysitters Club jobs. Mary Anne's, which was next, was sort of scary, as you'll see. And it was pretty interesting . . . at least to me.

10th
CHAPTER

Saturday, September 27

I don't know what Kristy always makes such a fuss about. Watson's kids are cute. Karen is five and Andrew is three. I think Kristy would like them if she ever baby-sat for them. Are you reading this Kristy? I hope so. Well, Kristy said this notebook is for us to write our experiences and our problems in, especially our problems.

And there were a few

problems at Watson's house. When I said Andrew and Karen were cute, I meant they were cute-looking. They were cute-acting, too, most of the time. But sometimes Karen was a pill. That was one problem. Another problem was Boo-Boo, the cat. The biggest problem was Mrs. Porter, the next-door neighbour. Anyone else who sits for Andrew and Karen should know about Boo-Boo and Mrs. Porter beforehand.

Watson picked Mary Anne up at 8.45 on Saturday morning and drove her to his house. He lives all the way across Stoney-brook, so it's hard to get to his place by bike.

According to Mary Anne, Watson was very nice to her in the car, which was to be expected. He always makes an extra effort to be nice to me, since he knows I don't like to have him round, so of course he would be nice to my best friend.

Mary Anne says that Watson lives in a very pretty, big house. I guess he has a lot of money. He'd have to, the way he throws it around, buying Chinese food right and left, and taking my mum out on dates almost every night. Anyway, the house is large, and Andrew and Karen have nice rooms. And *toys*. Mary Anne had never seen so many— gigantic stuffed animals, dolls, a train that you could really ride round the back garden, cars, bikes, a playhouse, costumes to dress up in. It was incredible, kind of like being in Toys 'R' Us.

Watson turned out to be not only a very good father, but a very organized customer. The first thing he did was introduce Mary Anne to Andrew and Karen, whose mother had just brought them over. Then he showed her their rooms, took her back downstairs, showed her where all the stuff was for making lunch, and finally pinned up a list of phone numbers she might need.

And then he brought out Boo-Boo.

From what Mary Anne told me, Boo-Boo must truly be a boo-boo. What a mess of a cat. He was grey with big yellow eyes that were kind of handsome, but he was *fat*. He looked like a pillow with legs attached. When he stood up, his stomach touched the ground, and when he tried to run, it swayed back and forth. He was huge.

"He weighs seventeen pounds," Karen said proudly.

"We think he belongs in the *Guinness Book of World Records*," remarked Watson.

Mary Anne couldn't work out why Watson was showing Boo-Boo to her. Okay, he was really, really fat. So what? Certainly he didn't need to be fed.

Watson cleared his throat and adjusted his glasses. "There are a few things you should know about Boo-Boo," he said.

Now, Mary Anne is not the bravest person in the world, and she said that right then she began to feel just the teensiest bit afraid. She put her finger in her mouth and bit at the nail.

"The first thing," said Watson, "is that Boo-Boo bites if provoked. And scratches."

"He's an attack cat," added Karen.

"It's best if you just steer clear of him," Watson went on. "I'd offer to confine him while I'm gone, but he doesn't like that much."

"He gnawed the laundry room door all up," said Karen.

"Just try to ignore him."

Mary Anne nodded.

"Whatever you do, don't touch him," added Watson.

Mary Anne nodded again.

"Well, I guess that's it. Any questions?"

"No, not really. Lunch at twelve-thirty,

right?" said Mary Anne.

"Right."

"What about Mrs Porter, Daddy?" asked Karen.

"Oh, I think she's on holiday," replied Watson. "No need to worry about her." He turned to Mary Anne. "Mrs Porter is an elderly woman who lives next door. She's a bit on the eccentric side and Karen is convinced she's a witch. She isn't, of course, but she doesn't like animals and Boo-Boo seems to have got on to her bad side. We try to keep the two of them apart. Okay, I'm off, kids." Watson kissed Andrew and Karen goodbye. "I'll be home by one-thirty," he told Mary Anne.

Mary Anne was just wondering how to entertain her charges when Karen began to talk. It turned out that she was a nonstop chatterer. "We're divorced," she announced.

"Yup," said Andrew.

"Our parents live in different houses."

"Yup," said Andrew. He sat down in a little wagon.

"Our mummy's going to get married again."

"Yup," said Andrew, pushing himself round the playroom.

"Then we'll have one mummy and two daddies."

"Yup," said Andrew. He backed into a bookcase.

"And if our daddy gets married again,

90

then how many mummies and daddies will we have, Andrew?"

"Yup."

Mary Anne giggled. "Come on, you two. It's a sunny day. Let's play outside, okay?"

"Oh, great!" exclaimed Karen. "I have a new doll. Daddy bought her for me. She hasn't been out in the sun much yet. I think she should get a tan, don't you? Dolls can tan, you know. Of course, they're real anyway. They can do whatever people can do. They can draw and breakdance and . . ."

Mary Anne was beginning to feel dizzy. "Want to play outside, Andrew?"

"Yup."

Mary Anne took the kids into Watson's big back garden. Andrew brought the wagon and pushed Boo-Boo round in it.

"Is he allowed to do that?" Mary Anne asked Karen. "Your father said not to touch Boo-Boo."

"Oh, he meant *you* shouldn't touch Boo-Boo. You're a stranger. But Boo-Boo knows us. He wouldn't hurt us." Karen paused for a breath and went on. "You see that house? The one next door?"

Mary Anne peered over Watson's rose beds and between the trees. Next door was a sprawling Victorian mansion, with gables and turrets and wooden curlicues on the porch. The paint was peeling and one shutter was crooked. Mary Anne said later it looked dark and scary.

"Yes?" she said to Karen.

"That's where the witch lives, right, Andrew?"

Andrew ploughed the wagon into a tree and Boo-Boo leaped out. "Yup."

"It's Mrs Porter, and she's an honest-and-truly witch. Mrs Porter isn't her witch name, though. Her witch name is Morbidda Destiny. The big kids in the street told me so. And she eats toads and casts spells and flies to witches' meetings on her broomstick every midnight."

Mary Anne stared at the house, nibbling away at her nails again. She wasn't sure what to tell Karen. If she told her the stories weren't true, she probably wouldn't get off to a very good start as a baby-sitter. If she agreed with Karen, she'd practically be lying to her. At last she asked, "Do you believe in the stories about Morb—Mrs Porter?"

Karen nodded. "I have proof."

"You do?"

"Yup. The proof is Boo-Boo. Mrs Porter made him fat. One day when Boo-Boo was nice and skinny, he went into Mrs Porter's garden and dug up some of her flowers. Mrs Porter came out and yelled at him and threw a fit. The next day he started getting fat."

"Yup," said Andrew.

"So now we have to keep Boo-Boo away from Mrs Porter's house. We don't want her to cast another spell on him. Making him fat wasn't so bad, but she might do something really, really mean."

"Well," said Mary Anne, "we don't have to worry about it today since Mrs Porter's not at home."

And it was at that *exact* second that Mary Anne saw a window shade snap up on the first floor of Mrs Porter's house. A wrinkled face with a big nose pressed itself against the panes of glass.

Karen saw the face, too. "Augh!" she screamed. "That's Morbidda Destiny! She's home after all! Where's Boo-Boo? Where's Boo-Boo?"

Mary Anne began to feel afraid again. She knew there were no such things as witches (were there?), but the face at the window didn't look very friendly. And Andrew was crying, and Karen was panicking.

"All right." Mary Anne tried to remain calm. She thought about what Watson had told her—that Mrs Porter was just an eccentric old lady. "Let's look for Boo-Boo," she said.

"We don't have to," wailed Karen. "I see him. He's—" Karen gulped. She pointed her finger. "He's in Morbidda Destiny's garden!"

"Well, I'll just go and get him—somehow," said Mary Anne, remembering that she wasn't supposed to touch Boo-Boo, let alone pick him up.

"She's already gone from the window!" Karen cried. "She's coming to the door! I know it."

"Okay, okay. Karen, you're in charge of Andrew for a few minutes. You stay in the garden with him and watch him. I'll be back."

Mary Anne said her heart was pounding as she crossed Watson's garden and stood at the edge of Mrs Porter's property. Boo-Boo was about ten feet away from her in the middle of some chrysanthemums, digging away happily.

"Boo-Boo," Mary Anne called softly. She glanced at the house. No sign of Mrs Porter. Maybe she hadn't seen Boo-Boo. "Boo-Boo," Mary Anne called again. "Come here." She snapped her fingers.

Boo-Boo didn't even look up.

"Yoo-hoo! Boo-Boo!" Mary Anne stepped closer. Boo-Boo sat down and scratched himself. "Boo-Boo. Hey, fat cat!"

"Boo-Boo. Hey, fat cat!" called a croaky voice.

Mary Anne's heart just about stopped beating. She whirled round. As she was whirling, she could hear Karen shrieking in Watson's yard. Behind Mary Anne stood ... a witch. "Honest to goodness," she told me later. "She looked just like a witch from a picture book."

Mrs Porter, or Morbidda Destiny or whoever she was, was dressed in black from head to toe. Her hair was grey and frazzly. There was a wart on the end of her nose. She was carrying what Mary Anne at first mistook for a broom, but which turned out to be a rake.

"That fat cat," said Mrs Porter, shaking the rake with every word, "is digging up my mums."

"I know, I know. I'm sorry. I'm trying to get him out for you." Mary Anne decided to forget Watson's warning. She stepped right into the garden and reached for Boo-Boo.

Boo-Boo hissed and swiped at her with his paw, claws extended.

Mary Anne jumped back.

"That does it, girlie," said Mrs Porter. She jumped into the garden and waved the rake at Boo-Boo.

Boo-Boo's eyes opened wide. He leaped over a bush of golden flowers, and streaked away. Luckily, he streaked back into Watson's garden.

Mrs Porter shook her rake after him. "Rapscallion!" she cried. She headed for her house. Mary Anne could hear her muttering things like, "Children and pets," and "Darned nuisance."

Back in Watson's garden, Karen greeted Mary Anne tearfully. "Did you hear that? It was a curse!"

"What was? 'Rapscallion'?" Mary Anne asked, looking nervously over her shoulder at the chrysanthemum bed.

"Yeah!"

"No, that wasn't a curse. That's a real word. She was calling Boo-Boo a name, but she did *not* put a spell on him."

"Are you sure?"

"Positive. Right, Andrew?"

"Yup."

"I don't know," said Karen. "I don't know."

"Look," Mary Anne went on. "Did you see Morb—Mrs Porter mixing up herbs or looking for bats' feet?"

"No . . ."

"Did you see her crushing toadstools or stirring things in a cauldron?"

"No . . ."

"Then how do you know she cast a spell?" asked Mary Anne triumphantly.

"She's a witch. She can do anything she w—Hey!" shrieked Karen, pointing.

Mary Anne's stomach flip-flopped. She immediately looked over at Mrs Porter's garden, sure she was going to see the old woman flapping across the lawn in her funny black dress. But Mrs Porter wasn't in sight. Karen was pointing at Boo-Boo.

"Look at that!" cried Karen. "He's going crazy."

Boo-Boo did, in fact, look a little crazy, Mary Anne said later. As she watched, the cat ran half-way across Watson's back garden, came to an abrupt stop, ran round in a circle, then dashed off in the direction he had just come from and scrambled up a tree.

"Oh," said Mary Anne nervously, "he's just being a cat. Cats do silly things like that all the time." Mary Anne had never owned a cat, so she'd had very little experience with them, but she had once seen the Pike's cat, Sarge, wake up from a sound sleep, leap off the couch, jump up on top of the television set, and immediately fall asleep again. Still . . .

"*Boo-Boo* doesn't do silly things," said Karen, edging toward Mary Anne. "He's too fat and old."

Mary Anne took Karen and Andrew by their hands. The three of them stood and watched Boo-Boo. For a while he looked as if he might go to sleep up in the tree.

Karen grew bored. "Psst," she whispered after a moment. "Morbidda Destiny's at her window again— and she's looking over here."

Sure enough, the old face was pressed against the windowpanes. Morbidda raised her right hand to her nose . . .

. . . and Boo-Boo sat straight up, slipped, slid, and finally fell out of the tree, landed on his feet, and shot past Mary Anne and the kids, hissing as he went by.

"Oh, *nooooo*," wailed Karen. Mary Anne squeezed her hand.

Boo-Boo tore up the steps to the back porch and waited by the door.

"I think it would be a good idea to let him in," said Mary Anne. "At least we won't have to worry about Mrs Porter's garden any more."

So Mary Anne opened the door and Boo-Boo ran inside. He ran straight into the laundry room, jumped into the laundry basket, and stayed there while Mary Anne and Karen and Andrew had lunch. Every time Mary Anne checked on him, he peered at her through the sides of the basket and yowled.

Mary Anne started to tell Karen that it was all just a big coincidence, but then she didn't know how to explain the meaning of coincidence, so she gave up.

"Daddy, it's a spell," Karen told Watson urgently as soon as he came home.

Watson laughed. "Don't be silly. There are no such things as spells."

But by then, even Mary Anne wasn't so sure. She was very relieved to go home.

11th CHAPTER

On the Wednesday after Mary Anne baby-sat for Watson's kids, Claudia, Mary Anne, Stacey, and I were holding a regular meeting of the Babysitters Club in Claudia's room. It was 5.45 and the phone had rung twice. The first call had been Mrs McKeever who was back in Stoneybrook. I'd said that, although Pinky and Buffy were very nice, we were not pet-sitters. The second call had been a new customer. Stacey had answered the phone. "Hello. Babysitters Club."

"Hello, my name is Mrs Marshall," said the voice on the other end. "I live in Rosedale Street. I got your flier, and I need a baby-sitter for Friday night. I'm sorry it's such short notice, but we had a baby-sitter lined up, and he had to cancel."

"Oh, that's okay," said Stacey. "Maybe I should tell you some things about the club, though, first. There are four of us and we're all twelve years old. On Friday nights, we can sit until ten. Well, one of us can."

"Oh, that's fine," replied Mrs Marshall. "My husband and I are just going out for dinner. We should be home about nine-thirty."

"Okay," said Stacey. "And how many children do you have?"

"Two."

"And how old are they?"

"Nina is three and Eleanor is one."

"Do you have any pets?"

(Some people seem a little surprised when we ask this question, but Mrs Marshall was okay about it.) "We have a cat. He's no trouble at all."

"And is there anything special the baby-sitter should know, or that she'd have to do?"

Mrs Marshall paused. (Aha! There's always a catch.) "Well, you'll have to give Eleanor her eardrops. She's getting over an ear infection. She always cries and makes a fuss, but in the end, she stays still and lets you put the drops in."

That didn't sound too bad. "Okay," said Stacey. "Let me find out who's available and I'll call you back."

As you can see, we'd learned a lot over the last couple of weeks.

Claudia took the job, since Stacey was mysteriously busy that night (she wouldn't tell us exactly what she was doing), and

Mary Anne's father and my mother get hysterical if we're not home by 9.30 on the dot. If Claudia was a little late, the Kishis wouldn't mind (much).

After we called Mrs Marshall back, I said, "Hey, why don't we work out how much money we've earned on our Babysitters Club jobs?"

"Okay!" said Stacey. She loved anything to do with money. Claudia handed her a piece of paper and a pencil. Then I opened our record book and read out the amount of money we'd been paid for each job. The total came to $26.75.

"Hey, that's not bad!" I exclaimed. "You know what we should do! We should each donate about three dollars and we could have a pizza party on Saturday afternoon."

"Yeah, a celebration of our club," said Claudia excitedly, "because it's a success!"

"We'll get Coke and crisps," I said.

"All the junk food we can eat," added Mary Anne happily.

Stacey remained silent.

"Oh, Stace," I said suddenly. "I'm sorry. We forgot about your diet. Maybe—"

"Oh, never mind." Stacey cut me off. "I may not be able to go anyway. We're, um, going to—New York on Friday and we might not be back in time for the party."

"Didn't you just go to New York?" asked Claudia.

"Well, yes, but there are a lot of things to

finish up. The move and all."

Claudia frowned. "I thought you said you finally got everything straightened out."

"Oh. We—we have to see some friends too. Oh, wow, it's six. I better go. Bye, you guys!"

Stacey tore out of Claudia's house.

Claudia and Mary Anne and I just looked at one another.

When I got home that evening, I found Watson parked on our living room couch reading the paper as though he lived at our house or something. I couldn't help making a face. Luckily, Watson didn't see it. In fact, he didn't look up from the paper until I was tiptoeing past the living room, trying to sneak into the kitchen without having to speak to him.

"Well, hi there, Kristy," he said cheerfully.

"Hello," I replied. I paused for a second, trying to decide whether I should say anything else, then gave up, and went on into the kitchen.

Mum must have just got home. She was reaching into the refrigerator, pulling out vegetables and leftovers for dinner. "Hi, sweetheart," she said. "How was school?"

"It was fine. Um, Mum, Watson's in our living room."

Mum smiled at me. "I know, silly. He

came home with me. I picked him up after work."

"Is he staying for dinner?"

Mum began slicing a tomato. "Yes, he is."

"Do you know this is the third time he's been over for dinner in the last week?"

"Kristy . . ."

"What did he bring us this time? Greek food? Italian?"

"Nothing," replied Mum smoothly. "He's here for leftovers."

That was definitely not a good sign. It meant Watson was through trying to impress us, and that Mum didn't feel she had to impress Watson any more, either. It meant they were getting more comfortable with each other. And it meant that Watson probably felt pretty comfortable with my brothers and me. Not a good sign at all.

Mum eyed me.

"What?" I said.

"Honey, would you please run upstairs and put on a dress?"

"A *dress*! Why?" I thought I looked all right in my school clothes. Besides, I never wear dresses if I can help it.

"Because I'm the mummy, that's why."

I giggled. Mum has a red T-shirt with that slogan across the front.

"Put on the blue and white one we've just bought, okay?"

I sighed. "Okay."

When I got upstairs, all my brothers were there brushing their hair. They had changed into decent shirts and pants. "What's going on?" I asked Sam.

He shrugged. "Something to do with Watson. Mum told us to dress up."

I made another face. I'm pretty good at faces. One thing I can do that no one else in our entire class can do—not even the boys—is turn my eyelids inside out. I did that then.

"Kristy, grow up," said Charlie. "That is really foul."

"It's scary," added David Michael.

"Sorry," I said. I helped him button his shirt.

Then I changed into my blue and white dress, purposely didn't brush my hair, and went downstairs. My brothers were helping Mum and Watson set the table in the dining room. Mum was lighting candles.

"Mum," I said, "will you please tell me what's happening? Why is everything so fancy?"

"Because we're celebrating."

"We're celebrating with leftover spaghetti?"

"It doesn't matter what we eat. I just want us feeling festive."

"Why? What are we getting festive about?"

Mum and Watson glanced at each other. Watson winked. "You'll see," said Mum.

"Mum, I don't feel too well," I said suddenly.

My mother sized me up in one half of a second. "Save it, Kristy," she said.

"Okay, okay, okay."

A few minutes later, we were sitting round the dining room table, which looked almost as fancy as it does at Christmas. Mum had spread out a green tablecloth and put a white runner over it. We were eating off our good china, and everyone had a wine glass. Mum and Watson were the only ones with wine in their wine glasses, though. David Michael's and mine were filled with milk. Sam and Charlie had put apple juice in theirs.

Spaghetti and apple juice. Some dinner.

We began passing round the leftovers. Mum and Watson didn't pay a bit of attention to what we kids chose for dinner. When everyone was served, Mum stood up at the head of the table and raised her glass. "Something very special happened today," she said.

I drew in my breath.

"Watson asked me if I would consider getting engaged to him."

I let the breath out.

"That's great, Mum," said Sam.

"Congratulations," said Charlie.

"Yeah!" cried David Michael, getting into the spirit of things.

"What does that mean?" I asked.

"It means your mother won't even let me give her an engagement ring yet," said Watson, smiling.

Smart move, Mum, I thought.

"But that I'm thinking about it," added Mum.

"Well," said Sam, "if engagement is one step away from marriage, does this mean you're two steps away?"

Mum and Watson laughed. "I suppose so," said Mum.

Good. Keep it that way.

"If you got married," I asked, "where would we live?"

"I don't know, honey," replied Mum. "We haven't thought that far ahead."

"Would we have to change schools?"

"I don't—"

"Would Karen and Andrew live with us, too? Would you keep on working? Would Dad still give you child-support money?"

"Kristy, I *don't know*. Now, enough questions. This is a celebration. We'll worry about those things later. Eat your—what is that you're eating?"

"Cake," I replied. "Cake and fried chicken."

"Eat your cake and fried chicken."

At that, everybody laughed.

I managed a tiny, forced smile. Very forced. I couldn't believe Mum's news. Why would she want to risk getting married again? My only hope was that she'd see the light before it was too late, and let our family return to normal.

12th
CHAPTER

The Babysitters Club planned its pizza party for Saturday afternoon. On Friday, during a regular meeting of the club, we pooled our money, except we only had nine dollars instead of twelve. That was because Stacey wasn't at the meeting. She and her parents had pulled out of their drive as soon as Claudia and I came home from school. Stacey waved to Claudia and me from the car window as they drove by us.

"They're on their way to New York," Claudia said. "Stacey told me at lunch today that they might be back tomorrow morning, or they might not be back until the evening."

"I wonder what we should do about the party."

"I don't know," replied Claudia slowly. "Let's talk about it at the meeting."

So we did.

"I think we should wait," said Mary Anne, curling up on Claudia's bed and pulling a bag of wine gums out of the pillowcase. "It'll be more fun if the whole club's at the party. We can have the party next weekend."

"But we really want to have it tomorrow, right?" said Claudia.

"Right," Mary Anne and I replied.

"So why don't we go ahead and buy everything except the pizzas tomorrow morning. If Stacey comes home, we can order the pizzas at the last minute and have the party. If she doesn't we'll keep the stuff until next weekend. Okay?"

So that was what we agreed to do. And that was what we *tried* to do. But it never happened.

The next morning, everything went wrong. Our house was in chaos. David Michael woke up with a stomach upset. Louie went sneaking through the living room, skidded on a rug, and hurt his paw. Mum was grouchy, Charlie couldn't find his football boots, and Sam overslept and nearly missed an emergency meeting of the Maths Club.

I myself was doing fine until the phone started ringing. The first call was from Mary Anne. She was crying. "mmfawolemspoomunno," she wailed.

"What? Mary Anne, I can't understand you. What's wrong?"

She slowed down and tried again.

"Your father?" I repeated. "Won't let you . . . spend your money . . . on what? On the *feet* of a *pauper*? . . . Oh, on the pizza party. . . . Oh, Mary *Anne*. You're kidding. Can't you talk to him?"

"I *tried*."

"Why won't he let you?"

"He says I should save the money I earn for more important, necessary things, like clothes and college."

"You mean you have to start paying for your clothes *yourself*?"

"I don't know. I don't think he does, either. He just won't let me spend three dollars on pizza. That's all."

"What a meanie."

"Yeah." Mary Anne blew her nose.

"Well, Claudia's got all the money. She can give yours back. We'll still have nine dollars when we get Stacey's share. I guess the four of us can make do with one large pizza. Stacey probably won't eat any, anyway."

"But Kristy, I'm not coming to the party now," said Mary Anne.

"Why not?"

"I'm not letting you all pay for ev—Just a second," she whispered. Then, "Okay, thanks for helping me with this maths," Mary Anne said loudly. "Now I understand what we're doing."

"Did your father just walk in?" I asked.

"Yes."

"Do you have to get off the phone now?"

"Yes. Listen, thanks again. I'll see you in school on Monday, Bye. June."

"*June?* Bye, Mary Anne."

So Mary Anne was the first person to drop out of the party.

The second phone call was from Claudia, who wasn't crying, but sounded like she might have been, or might be going to. "Guess what," she said angrily.

"What?"

"Mum and Dad got a letter from school in the post this morning saying how I'm not trying hard enough and don't pay attention and if I'd just concentrate on my work I could be a very good student."

"So? Don't you get one of those letters every autumn?"

"Yeah, but this time Dad had read it just before I told him and Mum about the pizza party, and he said no parties for me, it was time I started being more serious, and did I have any homework this weekend? When I said yes, he said he wanted me to spend all weekend on it."

"*All* weekend on ten maths problems?"

"Well, and on catching up on all the homework I haven't done so far this year."

"Oh."

"I'm sorry, Kristy."

"Me, too. But Mary Anne can't come either. I guess the party's off.

"Maybe not. I'm not through with my parents yet. Let's not say the party's off unless Stacey doesn't come home in time."

"Fine with me."

"All right. I'm going to go and start some of the maths. Now here's a question for you. When do you think we will ever need to know how to multiply fractions?"

"I don't know."

"Have you ever seen anyone besides teachers and maths students do it?"

"No."

"Do you need to do it in order to go shopping, cook dinner, or baby-sit?"

"No."

"I rest my case. School is stupid."

"Goodbye, Claudia."

"Goodbye."

The weirdest thing that morning happened with Stacey. Around 11.30, I decided to call the McGills to find out if they were home yet. Mrs McGill answered the phone and I introduced myself to her and asked for Stacey. There was a pause, then it sounded as if Mrs McGill might be covering up the mouthpiece of the phone, and then she got back on the line and said, "I'm sorry, dear, Stacey's not at home."

"Oh," I said, disappointed. "Where did she go?"

"Well, she's . . . um . . . she stayed in New York with friends, Kristy. She'll be back tomorrow night."

"Oh. Thank you," I said glumly. As soon as I hung up, the phone rang again. "Hello?" I said.

"Hi, it's me." Mary Anne.

"Hi! Did your father change his mind?"

"Are you kidding? I just wanted to be sure you knew Stacey was home. I was riding my bike to the Pikes'—that's where I am now; they called and asked me to sit this morning—and the McGills passed me in their car. Stacey didn't see me, though."

"Mary Anne, are you *sure* you saw Stacey in the car?" I said.

"Yeah, positive. She was sitting in the back wearing Claudia's trilby. Why?"

"Because I just spoke to Mrs McGill. She said Stacey decided to stay in New York with friends. Something funny is going on."

"Yeah," said Mary Anne slowly. "*Some-body's* lying. And it isn't me."

"Yeah . . . and it may not be *only* Mrs McGill," I added.

"What do you mean?" asked Mary Anne. "And make it quick. I've got to get off in a second."

"I mean that Stacey must have told her mother what to say. Mothers don't usually lie on their own. Stacey's so weird about food and dieting. She didn't want to come to the party in the first place. What is the matter with her, anyway?"

"I don't know, but I must go. Bye!"

I punched the button on the phone and

quickly began dialling again—just as Mum came into the kitchen, still looking grouchy.

"Kristy," she said, "how long have you been on the phone this morning?"

"Oh, *this* phone? For about an hour. On the hot line to the White House, for about—"

"Kristy . . ." said Mum warningly.

"Sorry. How's David Michael?" I asked.

"Better already. I think his bug will be short-lived."

"That's good." I turned back to the phone.

"Kristy . . ."

"Just one more call, Mum. It's important."

"Okay, *one* call. You know, you can go *over* to Mary Anne's and Claudia's. It's not as if they lived in Europe."

"Okay, okay. Last one." I dialled Claudia's number and she answered on the first ring.

"I'm trying to do my homework," she informed me crossly.

"This'll be short, I promise," I said. "There's something weird about Stacey. Mary Anne saw the McGills come home a little while ago, with Stacey in the back seat. But when I called them, Mrs McGill told me Stacey had decided to stay in New York. I think Stacey was there by the phone and just doesn't want to go to the party."

"Hmm," said Claudia, sounding puzzled.

"I don't know what that means. But if Mary Anne can't come to the party, and Stacey doesn't want to, and I'm not allowed to, I guess there's not much point in trying to have it."

"No," I agreed. We both got off the phone feeling depressed.

Immediately, the phone rang again.

"*Kristy!*" shouted my mother. "Get off the phone!"

"Do you want to answer it, Mum?" I asked. "I'm tired of it."

"All right." Mum lifted the receiver. "Hello?" she said brusquely, and then softly, "Oh, hel-*lo*."

It had to be Watson.

"How are you? . . . Yes? . . . Oh, no . . . Well, David Michael is sick . . . The Babysitters Club? Let me check with Kristy. What? . . . I don't know. I guess so. Sure . . . Twenty minutes. Someone will be ready. Goodbye, sweetheart.

"Kristy," Mum said before she'd even hung up the phone. "There's a little emergency. Watson needs one of you girls immediately. He needs someone to sit for his kids this afternoon. I'd tell him to drop them off here instead, but I'm afraid they'd catch David Michael's virus."

"Oh, Mum!" I cried. "It'll have to be *me*."

I didn't have a choice.

13th CHAPTER

Exactly twenty minutes later, Watson drove up with two little kids in the back seat. Mum ran me out to the car and practically shoved me in next to Watson. The emergency was that Watson's ex-wife (Andrew and Karen's mother) had fallen and broken her ankle and was in the emergency room at the hospital. Watson had to go over there and do something about insurance forms (I think) and also wait with her and take her home and make sure she could use the crutches okay and everything, since her future second husband was away for the weekend. Watson didn't want to make the kids hang round at the hospital with him.

Watson put his foot on the accelerator and vroomed us down the drive. I've never seen anyone in such a big hurry—and all over a broken ankle. If Watson could have flown the car back to his house I think he would have.

I wondered how Mum felt, seeing Watson go rushing off to his ex-wife. But I knew Watson's divorce was a friendly one, and also that some things (like insurance) still had to be straightened out. But Mum must have felt a little funny, anyway.

Watson talked a mile a minute during the drive, trying to tell me everything I'd need to know. I was glad I'd read the Babysitters Club Notebook, though, because he didn't say anything about Mrs Porter, the witch next door, or Boo-Boo the attack cat. I planned to keep the kids inside—or at least to keep Boo-Boo inside.

"The children are Andrew and Karen," said Watson breathlessly. "Andrew is three and Karen is five. They're about ready for their lunch. Peanut butter and jam is fine. Karen can help you find things. Emergency numbers are by the phone, but since I'll be at the hospital, if there's a real emergency it would probably be easier to call your mum."

"Okay," I said, feeling a bit dazed.

"Around two o'clock, Andrew has a sleep. I guess that's all you need to know. I wish I could take the time to show you everything, but Karen will have to fill in for me, okay, darling?"

"Okay!" said Karen.

"Good girl." Watson screeched to a halt in front of a big white house in one of the

116

fanciest neighbourhoods in Stoneybrook. A wide green lawn stretched all round it, interrupted by old trees and little flower gardens. I looked for the witch's house as I got out of the car. "Be good kids," said Watson. "And Kristy, thank you. I want you to know that I really appreciate this."

I held the back door open and Andrew and Karen scrambled out of the car. "See you later!" called Watson. He rushed off.

I stood in Watson's front garden and looked at Andrew and Karen. Baby-sitting for them was absolutely the last thing I wanted to do.

I sighed heavily. "All right. Are you guys hungry?"

"Starving," said Karen. "You know what I had for breakfast? Just toast. Toast and orange juice. I wanted crisps, but Mummy said no 'cause they're junk food. Sometimes Daddy lets us have them, though. He does and Mummy doesn't. Isn't that silly? I think it's really silly."

"Are *you* hungry, Andrew?" I asked.

"Yup."

"Well, let's go and get some lunch, then.

We went through the front door of Watson's house, and the first thing I saw was not the huge, georgeous front hall, not the tree that was growing in the living room, not the sparkling chandelier or the stained glass window, but a fat creature that could only be Boo-Boo.

Sure enough. "Hello, Boopa-de-Boo," cried Karen, hugging him. "This is Boo-Boo," she told me. "He's Daddy's cat. He's really old. Daddy had him even before he knew our mummy. Did you know he's had two spells put on him by a *witch*? She lives next door in the scary house."

I sighed again. It was going to be a long day. "Come on. Let's get our lunch," I said.

In the kitchen, Karen helped me find the stuff for sandwiches, and then I made apple slices and carrot sticks and poured us each a glass of milk.

"Yum," said Karen. "Yummy-yummers! You're a nice baby-sitter. You make good food."

"Yup," said Andrew.

Karen ate a few bites of her sandwich, then suddenly looked at me very seriously, her brown eyes glistening. "Is our mummy all right?" she asked me.

"Oh, of *course*," I replied. "A broken ankle isn't too serious. She'll have to wear a cast and walk on crutches for a while, but in a few weeks she'll be all better. Having a cast is fun. Everyone signs it and draws pictures on it."

"Did you ever have a cast?" asked Karen.

"Last summer," I replied. "I broke my ankle, just like your mummy."

"How did you do it?"

"I was taking our dog, Louie, for a walk—"

118

"You have a dog? Can I see him some-time?" interrupted Karen, wiping away a milk-moustache.

"I expect so," I answered. "Anyway I was taking Louie for a walk, except I was riding my bike. Louie was on his lead, running next to me. We came to a tree. Louie went one way, I went the other, the lead wrapped around the tree, and *whoosh*! I flew off my bike."

Karen giggled. Even solemn Andrew managed a tiny smile. I was beginning to feel better. Mary Anne was right. Karen and Andrew weren't too bad— considering Watson was their father.

"So that's how I broke my ankle. I had to wear a cast for six weeks. I couldn't go swimming all summer."

"Yuck," said Karen.

"Yuck," said Andrew. It was a nice change from "Yup." He went back to his lunch, which he was eating slowly and neatly. Take a bite, chew, chew, chew, chew, chew, chew, chew, swallow, wipe mouth, start again.

Karen ate silently, too, for a moment, and I could tell she was thinking about some-thing. At last she put the remains of her sandwich on her plate and said, "you're Kristy, right?"

"Right," I replied.

"Is your mummy Edie Thomas?"

"That's right." The kid was smart.

"My daddy says he loves your mummy."

"I guess," I said uncomfortably. I realized that Karen looked uncomfortable, too.

"If they get married, your mummy will be my mummy."

"Stepmummy, I mean stepmother," I corrected her. "And guess what. I'd be your stepsister. And yours, Andrew."

"Yup," said Andrew.

Karen thought for a while again. "That would be okay," she said at last. And then, "Do you like being divorced, Kristy?"

"Not particularly," I said.

"How come?"

"Because I never see my father. He moved to California. That's far away."

"Ooh," said Karen. "We don't like being divorced either, but we see our daddy lots."

"I know," I said dryly. Boy, did I know. Watson, the perfect divorced father.

"Our mummy's getting married again."

"I know."

"We don't want her to, do we, Andrew?"

"Yup."

"You don't?" I said.

"Nope. Mummy says oh we're so lucky, we'll have two daddies, and maybe someday two daddies and two mummies. But we just want our old mummy and daddy—all in one house."

"I know what you mean." Karen was all right.

Suddenly I was aware of little sniffling

sounds next to me. Andrew was crying into his sandwich crusts. Karen jumped up and ran round the table to hug her brother. "I'm sorry, Andrew," she said. "I'm sorry."

"What's wrong?" I asked nervously.

"He doesn't like to hear about all the mummies and daddies. I'm not 'asposed to talk about it too much."

"Oh." I wiped Andrew's tears with my napkin. "Hey, you kids, how about a special treat? Ice cream for dessert!"

"At *lunchtime*?" asked Karen incredulously.

"Sure," I said, opening the freezer door and hoping I'd find ice cream inside. Luckily, there was almost a whole carton of chocolate ripple. "Divorced kids are special kids. How about it, Andrew?"

Andrew's eyes lit up. "Okay," he sniffled. "That's good."

"All *right*!" I ruffled his hair.

I placed three bowls of chocolate ripple ice cream on the table and we ate away happily. Karen was so happy, she couldn't even speak. As we were slurping up the last dribbles, Boo-Boo waddled into the kitchen. Karen jumped up and ran to the back door.

"Wait!" I cried. "Karen, don't let him out, okay?"

"But he wants to go. He's allowed."

"Is Mrs Porter home?" I asked.

Karen stepped away from the door. "Oh. . . . I don't know."

"Maybe we better keep him inside. Just until your dad comes back, okay?"

"Yeah," said Karen. "Good idea."

"But *we* can go out," I added. I decided that would be all right, as long as we didn't go near Mrs Porter's garden.

"Because divorced kids are special kids," said Andrew.

"You've got it," I said.

Andrew giggled. "You've got it? That's funny!"

Andrew and Karen and I played hide-and-seek until it was time for Andrew's rest. Then Karen and I sat on the back porch and read *Little Toot* and *The Snowy Day* and *The Tale of Mrs Tiggy-Winkle*. We were halfway through *The Little Engine That Could* when Watson came home.

"How is she?" I asked. I wasn't sure what to call Watson's ex-wife. I didn't even know her name.

"At home and on her feet," he replied. "Or at any rate, on her foot. She's okay. But you kids," he said to Karen, "are going to stay with me for the rest of the weekend so Mummy can rest, okay?"

"Goody!" said Karen.

"How did everybody get along?" asked Watson.

"Fine," I answered. Suddenly I felt shy.

"Daddy, I like Kristy," Karen announced. "I don't mind if she's going to be our stepsister."

122

Watson smiled, but I blushed. "Well, I'm glad everything went so well," he said.

"Does she have to go home now?" asked Karen.

"Well, she won't be able to if Andrew is asleep. Is he?"

"He went down about—" I checked my watch—"almost an hour ago."

"Hmm," said Watson. "I don't really want to wake him up. Do you want to call your mum and get her to pick you up?"

"I better not," I said. "She probably won't want to leave David Michael."

"Do you mind waiting? Andrew shouldn't sleep more than another half hour or so."

"I don't mind." And I didn't. I really didn't. While we waited for Andrew, Watson took turns playing draughts with Karen and me. He won every game. I was glad because if he'd *let* me win, it would have proved he was trying too hard to make us feel like one big happy family.

Later, as Watson was driving me home, Karen said, "Kristy, I wish you were our big stepsister, right now."

"Well," I said, "how about if I am your baby-sitter instead?"

"That's okay," said Karen.

"Yeah, that's okay," echoed Andrew.

I glanced at Watson. He was sneaking a look at me, too. We smiled at each other.

That night after Mum had got David

Michael to sleep, she came into my room. I was writing up my experience at Watson's in the Babysitters Club Notebook.

"So," she said, "now that we have a moment to ourselves, tell me how everything went at Watson's. I'm sorry that was thrown at you today, but maybe it worked out for the best."

I was glad Mum wasn't saying, I told you so.

"It went okay," I said. "Andrew and Karen are cute. Andrew hardly ever talks, though. Karen says the divorce upsets him."

"It does upset him," Mum said, "but he's also got a big talker for an older sister. He almost doesn't *need* to speak."

"Karen sure is a big talker," I agreed. "I think she's really smart."

"She is. She's just started school, and her teacher is already thinking of putting her into the next class after Christmas."

"Wow," I said.

"Kristy, would you baby-sit for Watson's children again, if he needed you?"

"I've already told Karen that since I can't be her stepsister yet, at least I'd be her baby-sitter."

My mother looked pleased.

"Mum?" I asked. "What will happen when you and Watson get married? I mean, *if* you get married. Would Andrew and Karen live with us? Would we all live in

Watson's house? It's so big."

"Does it bother you that there are no arrangements yet?"

"Yes," I replied. "I like to know what's going to happen."

"I'm afraid I can't tell you anything definite, honey."

"Can you tell me something *un*definite?"

Mum smiled. "Well, first of all, Watson's custody arrangements probably won't change, so wherever we live, Andrew and Karen won't live with us. They'll only visit. And right now, it looks as though we might move to Watson's, simply because there's more space."

"But I don't want to move!"

"Kristy, I said 'might'."

"Okay."

"Time to get ready for bed now. Goodnight, sweetheart."

" 'Night, Mum."

14th CHAPTER

On Monday at our next meeting of the Babysitters Club, everyone seemed to be back to normal. And most of us had news.

"Guess what!" Mary Anne said, in between phone calls.

"What?" Claudia and Stacey and I said.

"Dad and I hardly talked to each other all day Saturday, but on Sunday, I decided to go ahead and try reasoning with him about the money I earn, since I thought I didn't have anything to lose. I told him I'd be earning a lot of money through the Babysitters Club, and I asked him if I could spend half of it any way I wanted—*if* I promised to put the other half in the bank. And he said yes! So if we have the party, I can go!"

"Great!" I cried. "Hey, that's wonderful! You really stood up to your dad."

"Yeah. . . ." Mary Anne looked

embarrassed, but I knew she was pleased with herself.

"I have some good news, too," Claudia said. "I caught up on almost all of my homework, and I got a B-minus on those ten maths problems. *And* last night *I* had a talk with *my* parents. I told them I wasn't Janine and they said they knew that. Then they said I had to start setting aside time for my homework every day. At first I thought Dad was going to say no more baby-sitting, but instead he said an hour or so after dinner would be all right, and he and Mum and Janine and Mimi would help me. That cuts into my TV time, but I'd rather give up TV than art or baby-sitting and the club." Claudia reached under her mattress and pulled out some liquorice sticks, which of course she passed round and of course Stacey refused.

"Well, that's good," said Mary Anne. "I'm proud of us, aren't you, Claudia?"

"Yeah," said Claudia.

I wanted to tell my good news about sitting for Watson's kids, but I was more curious about Stacey and why she had done what she did.

"So, Stace," I said brightly. "How was your weekend? How was New York?"

"Oh, it was fine. I went shopping at Bloomingdale's and bought this." She indicated the tartan wool trousers she was wearing, which were held up with bright red braces. "I got a matching hat, too."

"Nice," I said. "How were your friends?"

"Fine." Stacey was picking at a piece of fuzz on her trousers, carefully not looking at the rest of us.

"It must have been fun to spend so much time with them."

"Yeah."

"You know, the strangest thing happened on Saturday morning," I said. As usual, I couldn't help it. I was dying to say what I knew. There would be no stopping me despite the fact that Claudia was sending me an urgent telegram with her eyes. *Shut up*, they were saying. *Don't do this.* But it was too late, even though I knew it was going to cause problems. Even though I knew that Claudia still considered Mary Anne and me babies, and Stacey sophisticated, and therefore was going to protect Stacey and whatever she was up to.

"Mary Anne saw you come home with your parents on Saturday," I said. "How come you made your mum say you stayed in New York?"

Stacey's head jerked up, her eyes flashing. She looked as though she wanted to kill Mary Anne or me or possibly both of us. "Are you accusing my mum of lying?" she cried.

I thought for a moment. "I guess so."

Stacey stood up, hands on her hips. "Kristy, you—you—"

See, the thing is, right then, if Stacey wanted an "out", she had one. She could have blamed the whole thing on her mother by saying her mother was punishing her that weekend or something, and boy, weren't parents awful. But she didn't do that. She just blew up. And she didn't give any reason for why she and her mum were lying, which, Mary Anne said later to me in private, only proved that Stacey (and her mother) were covering something up.

Anyway, Stacey stood in Claudia's room, glowering at me. "I can't believe you just said that, Kristy. You're such a baby."

"You don't have any tact at all," added Claudia, immediately jumping to Stacey's defence, as I had know she would.

Mary Anne remained silent. She hates arguments.

"Well, how do you think I feel, being lied to?" I shouted. "Talk about tact. It made me feel like a little kid."

"You *are* a little kid," said Claudia. "Look at how you're dressed."

I looked. "What's wrong with the way I'm dressed?"

"Really, Kristy, a sweater with snowflakes and snowmen on it? You look like a four-year-old."

"Well, *you've* got sheep slides in your hair," I yelled. "You think they're adult?"

"Sheep," Claudia informed me witheringly, "are *in*."

"Who cares? Everything's in *some*time. First it was frogs, then pigs, now it's sheep. Maybe next week it'll be snowmen. And how do you expect me to keep up with that stuff, anyway? I don't have time for it."

"That's because you and Mary Anne are too busy playing with dolls."

"*Dolls!*" I yelled. (Mary Anne looked as if she'd been slapped in the face. I knew she was going to start crying soon, and it only made me angrier.) "*We do not play with dolls!*" The thing is, though, that we only gave up over the summer.

At that moment, surprisingly, Mary Anne spoke up. "Claudia, Kristy didn't mean to upset Stacey." Mary Anne's chin was trembling. Her eyes were about to overflow.

"Didn't mean to upset her! She accused her mother of lying."

Mary Anne's eyes spilled over.

"Oh, what a crybaby," Claudia said, but I could see she felt bad.

Suddenly a knock came on the door.

"*What!*" yelled Claudia.

The door opened a crack. I was terrified that Janine was going to be on the other side of it with some stupid comment like there's no such word as *crybaby*.

But it was Mimi who poked her head in. "Excuse me, girls," said Claudia's grandmother in her gentle, slightly accented voice, "but what is going on in here? Downstairs I can hear you. You are yelling.

What is wrong, and may I help you in some way?"

We all grew quiet. I felt slightly ashamed. "I'm sorry, Mimi," said Claudia. We'd all been standing up about ready to kill each other, and now we found places to sit down again.

"Are you girls all right? May I help?" Mimi asked again.

"No, thank you," said Claudia, sounding subdued. "We didn't mean to be so loud."

"All right. If you need me, I will be in the kitchen. Claudia, your friends must leave in fifteen minutes."

"Okay."

Mimi tiptoed out and closed the door softly behind her. I looked at the four of us and saw that we were sitting as if we were at war: Mary Anne next to me on the floor, Claudia and Stacey together on the bed. We were like two gangs.

The phone rang.

"I'll get it," we all said, and leaped for the phone, each of us determined to answer it. Stacey and I got to it first and both grabbed it off the hook. We had a real tug-of-war, yanking it back and forth, before I jerked it out of Stacey's grip.

"Babysitters Club," I said gruffly. "Yes? . . . Yes? It was a new client. He needed a sitter for Thursday after school for his seven-year-old daughter. I took down all the information, and said that I'd get back to him in five minutes.

"Well?" said Claudia after I'd hung up the phone.

Stacey was so mad she had turned red. No kidding. She couldn't even speak.

"Who's free Thursday afternoon?" I asked. "It's a seven-year-old kid, Charlotte Johanssen, on Kimball Street."

"I'm free," said Claudia.

"So'm I," Stacey managed to say through clenched teeth.

"Me, too," said Mary Anne timidly.

"Me, too," I added.

We glared at one another.

"Well, now what?" said Stacey.

"Yeah." Claudia narrowed her eyes. "Whose dumb idea was this club, anyway? Four people all wanting the same job. That's stupid."

"Since the club was *my* dumb idea," I snapped, "*I'll* take the stupid job." And I did. After I'd hung up the phone for the second time I said to Mary Anne, "Come on, let's go. I can see we're not wanted *here*."

Claudia looked a bit sheepish. "Kristy..." she said hesitantly.

"Save it. I'm not speaking to you at the moment."

Mary Anne and I left the house without bothering to say goodbye to Mimi. Mary Anne was crying again. I almost said something nasty to her, but realized that if I did, the four of us might become three against one, which was definitely worse than two against two.

"Don't cry," I said at last.

"I'm sorry. I just hate fighting, that's all."

"Me, too. But we'll all be friends again soon."

"I suppose so."

"I know so. We've got the club to hold us together, right?"

"Right," agreed Mary Anne.

But she didn't sound very sure, and I didn't feel very sure.

So even though I was worried about the fight and sorry we'd had it, I believed that it would all blow over soon enough. And by later that evening, I heard such astonishing news that I forgot all about the fight anyway.

Mum and Watson had gone out to dinner, and my brothers and I had finished our homework and were sitting round the kitchen table playing Monopoly. Well, Charlie and Sam and I were playing Monopoly. David Michael, who had fully recovered from his virus, was busy making G.I. Joe attack a ferocious enemy Kleenex box. Sam had just bought all four stations and was cleaning Charlie and me out, when the back door opened and in walked Mum and Watson. We hadn't expected them home so early.

"Surprise!" cried Mum, coming into the kitchen. Watson threw a handful of confetti over her.

My brothers and I smiled. "What's going on?" asked Charlie.

Mum and Watson looked at each other, eyes sparkling.

I got a funny feeling in the pit of my stomach.

"You tell them," said Watson.

Mum turned to us. She looked radiant. "I agreed to become engaged," she said.

Already?

Mum held up her left hand. There was a ring on her fourth finger with a diamond on it about the size of a boulder.

"Wow," I couldn't help saying.

We all crowded around to look at the ring. "It's pretty," said David Michael.

"It means Watson is going to be your stepdaddy," Mum told him.

"Really-really-really?" David Michael jumped up and down. Sam hugged Mum, and Charlie shook Watson's hand. But I just stood there. I wasn't upset, but I wasn't happy either. I could only think of questions. Finally, I asked just one. "When will the wedding be?"

"Oh, not for months," replied Mum.

I let out a sigh. That was definitely a relief.

15th
CHAPTER

On Tuesday, Mary Anne and I avoided Claudia and Stacey in school until the very end of the day. Then I screwed up the nerve to ask Claudia if she wanted to hold a Babysitters Club meeting the next day as usual. She said it was all right with her.

That night, for a change, Mum and my brothers and I went over to Watson's for dinner. Andrew and Karen were there. Watson was taking care of them more often than usual since their mother had broken her ankle.

Karen was in rare form. She loved having company and spent a long time trying to straighten out all the relationships. "If my daddy and your mummy get married—" she started to say to me, hopping from one foot to the other while Watson passed a plate of potato crisps and onion dip round the living room.

"*When* we get married," Watson interrupted her.

"Okay, *when* you get married, Kristy, you'll be my stepsister, and Charlie, you'll be my biggest stepbrother . . . How old are you, anyway?"

"Guess," said Charlie.

"Thirty-five?"

That broke Charlie up. "Thirty-*five*! That's practically over the—"

"Watch what you say, young man," said Mum. "If thirty-five is over the hill, then I'd better start saving for false teeth and a wheelchair now."

Everyone laughed.

"Twenty-nine?" Karen guessed.

"No!" said Charlie. "I'm sixteen."

Karen stared at him. "Okay," she said at last. She turned to Sam. "You'll be my next biggest stepbrother."

"Yeah, and you know how old I am? A hundred and twelve."

I giggled. So did Karen.

"And you'll be my last stepbrother," she said to David Michael. (It was a good thing she hadn't said "my littlest stepbrother".)

"Do you know how old I am?" he asked.

I hoped Karen was more accurate with little people than big ones, because David Michael is very touchy about his age. He hates people to think he's younger than six.

"Eight?"

I breathed a sigh of relief. David Michael beamed.

"Want to see my room?" Karen asked him.

"Sure!"

David Michael and Karen ran up the stairs, with Andrew at their heels.

I sat back in my chair and looked around the living room. There was no carpet, just little rugs with the wooden floor, all polished, in between. In one corner of the room was a small tree in a brass tub. At one end was a huge fireplace. Near the other end was a gleaming grand piano. I decided I liked the room. I decided I could get used to it if I had to.

Dinner was fun. Watson made fondue. He set a big pot full of hot, melty cheese in the middle of the table. Then he gave everyone a long fork and a plate of pieces of French bread. You were supposed to spear a piece of bread with your fork, dip it in the cheese, and eat it. Watson made this rule that if your bread fell off your fork and landed in the cheese, you had to kiss the person sitting on your right.

"Ew! Yuck!" said David Michael.

Then everyone began making rules. "If you drip cheese on the tablecloth," said Charlie, "you can't eat for two minutes."

"If you knock someone's bread off his fork, you become his slave for the evening," I said.

Everyone was really careful after that.

And then it happened. I was just sticking my fork into the pot when my bread fell off and landed in the cheese. Guess who was on my right. Watson.

I couldn't even look up. Maybe no one had noticed what I'd done.

But *every*one had.

"Oo-oooh, Kris-*tee*," teased Sam.

"Kiss Daddy, kiss Daddy!" cried Karen.

I glanced across the table and saw Mum watching me. I bet she thought I wouldn't do it, that I'd make a scene. Well, I'd show her.

I leaned over, gave Watson a peck on the cheek that was so fast you probably couldn't even have timed it, and went back to my dinner.

Later, when we were cleaning up the kitchen, I began to feel a little guilty. I mean, I could have been nicer about the kiss. So I sneaked into the den, found a piece of paper, and wrote Watson this note:

Dear Watson,
The next time you need a baby-sitter for Andrew and Karen, please call me first. I would be happy to do the job.

> *Yours truly,*
> *Kristy*

P.S. The fondue was fun.

P.P.S. I like your house.

P.P.P.S. If you and Mum want to get married, it's okay with me.

I almost wrote "Love, Kristy" then, but I didn't want to get mushy, so I didn't say anything else. I taped the note to Watson's bathroom mirror.

The next day, Mary Anne and I walked to Claudia's house for the club meeting. We went together, sort of as protection. When we reached Claudia's room, we found her talking to Stacey. When we entered, the talking stopped. Silence.

Mary Anne and I sat down. I was determined not to be the first one to speak, since I felt I had already made an effort by asking whether we were going to hold a meeting that day.

At long last, Claudia said, "I'm sorry I was so mean yesterday. I'm sorry I yelled." She was looking at Mary Anne, but not at me.

"That's okay," said Mary Anne.

"And I'm sorry I lied," said Stacey.

"Claudia, are you only sorry about making Mary Anne cry, or are you also sorry you yelled at *me*?" I asked.

Claudia sighed. "Kristy," she said. "I'm sorry I lost my temper. I really am. I had no reason to yell at Mary Anne, but *you* made

139

me angry."

"How?" I demanded.

"You know how."

I looked at the floor. "By butting into someone else's business. By opening my mouth."

"Yeah."

"Well, I *did* tell a lie," said Stacey.

"But your lie didn't hurt anybody," said Claudia. "At least, as far as I know. And you must have had a good reason for lying, especially since your mum went along with you. Whatever it was, Kristy shouldn't have accused you like she did. It was just plain rude. You're a friend, and I don't want anyone to hurt you."

"But I'm your friend, too," I said.

"Right," agreed Claudia. "And I don't like my friends to be rude. If you weren't my friend, I wouldn't bother to tell you this. If you weren't my friend, you wouldn't be worth getting mad at."

I thought that over. "I have one thing to say about being lied to. I don't like it. And I have a right to say so." I had a feeling we weren't going to clear up the business of Stacey's lie, and that bothered me. But it was time to smooth things over. "I have something else to say, too. I'm really going to try to watch my mouth from now on. I mean it. My mouth gets me in trouble all the time. Just ask my mother."

"Just ask anybody," said Claudia.

We all giggled.

"Once, right after my grandmother came back from the hairdressers, I asked her why she had had her hair dyed purple," I said. "I was really in trouble then."

"Once I cried in front of my whole class," Mary Anne admitted.

"Oh, that's so embarrassing for a little kid," said Stacey knowingly.

"Little kid! It was last week!"

More giggling.

Then the phone rang and we got down to business.

At six o'clock I said, "I've got a great idea! Now that we've all straightened out our problems, I think we should try to have the pizza party again. Stace, you *really* don't have to worry about your diet. We can get you a salad at the pizza place, if you don't want pizza. They make really good salads."

"All right," she said slowly.

"And," I added, thinking of Stacey and Sam, "we can have the party at my house."

Stacey's eyes lit up. "O-*kay!* I'll be there."

"Is Saturday all right with everyone?" I asked.

We settled on Saturday at five o'clock. In the back of my mind, I was thinking that maybe I could talk Mum into a slumber party, and five seemed like a good hour for a sleep-over to begin.

141

Mum was easily talked into a slumber party. She liked the Babysitters Club. "After all," she told me, "it brought you and Watson closer together."

I nodded. "The club has helped all of us. It helped Stacey make some friends. I think it helped give Mary Anne the courage to stand up to her father. And it showed Claudia that she can be good at something besides art, even if it's not a genius kind of thing like Janine's good at." I was pretty pleased with our club, and I was glad Mum was pleased, too.

On Saturday at five o'clock, Mary Anne, Claudia, and Stacey came round to my house, and our fabulous pizza-slumber party began. We ate and ate and ate. Well, Claudia and Mary Anne and I ate. Stacey had a helping of salad and an apple, and later in the evening she drank a diet soda and even joined the rest of us in some popcorn.

At eleven we put on our nightdresses and spread our sleeping bags out on the floor of the bedroom. Stacey had a really spectacular nightshirt with gold glitter and the skyline of New York City across the front.

"Gosh," said Mary Anne, "you are so lucky to have lived in New York, and to get to take trips there all the time. I've only been twice."

Stacey pressed her fingers together. She closed her eyes for a moment, then opened them and said, "You guys, I have something to tell you."

"What?" I said eagerly. It sounded like a big confession was coming up.

Claudia gave me a look that said, Watch what you say.

I closed my mouth.

"I have a secret," Stacey began.

It was all I could do not to cry out, "I knew it! I knew you were hiding something."

"You know the diet I'm on? Well, it's not just any old diet. And the trips to New York? They're not just to visit friends. I have to go to a doctor there. Sometimes I have to stay in the hospital overnight."

Claudia and Mary Anne looked stricken. "Oh, Stace," I said softly. "I knew it. You have anorexia, right? That's what the crazy diet is all about."

"Anorexia?" repeated Stacey. "No."

No?

"I have—I have diabetes," she managed to say. "I just got it last year."

Mary Anne opened her eyes wide.

"Oh, poor Stacey," said Claudia, giving her an awkward hug.

But I said, "Diabetes? Is *that* all?"

"Is that *all*?" exclaimed Stacey. "What do you mean?"

"Well, I mean . . . why didn't you just tell us? My cousin Robin has diabetes. It means you have a problem with sugar. Your body doesn't process it the way most people's bodies do. Too much or too little sugar can be dangerous, right? And you probably have to give yourself insulin shots every day. It's rotten, but I mean, you're not a freak or something. We'll stop offering you sweets, okay?"

Claudia gave me another look. This one meant, sincerely, Good going, Kristy.

"But don't you care?" asked Stacey.

"Of course we care," I replied.

"I mean, doesn't it bother you?"

"No. Why should it?" said Claudia frowing.

"Yeah," said Mary Anne and I.

"I don't know. My mother acts like it's some kind of curse. The kids at my old school started teasing me about my diet, and because I fainted a couple of times, so Mum decided we should come to a 'peaceful little town'. You know, get me to some place 'civilized and quiet'."

"That's why you moved here?" said Mary Anne incredulously.

Stacey nodded. "Well, partly."

"Wow," I said.

"So I thought maybe I should cover up what was wrong with me. Moving here seemed like a chance to start again. But *not* telling you people was worse than *telling* my old friends. It got so complicated with the lies and everything."

"Well," said Mary Anne in her quiet

way, "maybe you don't have to tell *all* the kids. We know, and that's important because we see you most often. Maybe you could sort of keep quiet about it at school—but not lie about it."

"That's true," agreed Stacey. Her face softened. "You lot are great."

We smiled.

"I think we should have a slumber party once a month," she exclaimed.

"Yeah," I said. "When Mum and Watson get married, we'll have them at Watson's house, if we move there. The third floor would be perfect. We would have it all to ourselves."

"When your mother and Watson get *married*!" cried Claudia.

I nodded. Then I told my friends everything.

Just as I was finishing, a knock came on the door. "Hey, all you girls!" called Sam's voice. "Mum said to bring this to you. Don't worry, I'm not coming in. I'm leaving it outside the door. Now I'm walking down the hall. Now I'm going down the stairs . . ." His footsteps faded away.

I opened the door and found a tray with four glasses, a bottle of diet soda, an apple, a packet of biscuits, a note from Mum that said she left lots of food so we wouldn't have to raid the refrigerator.

I brought the tray inside.

"Your brother's so cute, Kristy," said Stacey.

"I guess. For a boy."

"No, really . . . Do you like any boys, Kristy?"

I made a face.

"What do—" Stacey started to say, but I held my finger to my lips.

"Shh!" I hissed. "Do you hear that?"

"What?"

"Something at the window."

We made ourselves quiet. We couldn't hear a sound.

"I guess it's nothing," I said. But while we were all in the mood, I turned out the lights and whispered to the others, "What's the scariest thing that ever happened while you were baby-sitting?"

In hushed voices we began telling about creepy nights sitting up in silent houses, waiting for parents to come home. Then we started telling ghost stories.

I felt deliciously scared—and happy. We were friends again. Things were okay with Watson. The Babysitters Club was a success. I, Kristin Amanda Thomas, had made it work, or helped to make it work. I hoped that Mary Anne, Claudia, Stacey, and I—the Babysitters Club—would stay together for a long time.

CLAUDIA AND THE
PHANTOM
PHONE CALLS

Book 2

CLAUDIA AND THE
PHANTOM PHONE CALLS

1st
CHAPTER

The evening was gloomy and windy, with rain streaming down from heavy clouds that blocked the moon. I thought it was the perfect night to a) curl up with *The Phantom of Pine Hill*—a really spooky Nancy Drew mystery—and the liquorice bootlaces I'd hidden in my desk, or b) work on the still life I'd started and daydream about Trevor Sandbourne. But "No," my dad said, "homework first, Claudia," and there's no arguing with Dad. Besides, we have an agreement, my parents and I. The agreement is that if I get all my homework done every night (with someone in my family supervising me), I can continue to take my art classes. More important, I can stay in the Babysitters Club.

The Babysitters Club is something my friend Kristy Thomas thought up a little while ago at the beginning of the school year. Kristy, who lives across the street from me, does a lot of baby-sitting. So do I, Claudia Kishi, and so does Kristy's best friend, Mary Anne Spier, who lives next door to Kristy. So Kristy had this idea that the three of us should get together to form a group of baby-sitters, advertise ourselves, and have a little business, which is just what we did. Then we asked a new friend of mine, Stacey McGill, to join, which *she* did. The Babysitters Club is working really well. People know about us and call us all the time, and each of us has more jobs now than before the Babysitters Club, so it was important that I be allowed to stay in it. But I almost blew it when the school sent a letter home to my parents saying that I wasn't working up to potential and things like that. My parents are used to those letters—they get them about twice a year—but what they hadn't expected to find out was that I had done almost none of my homework since school started. That was when Mum and Dad laid down the law.

The thing about homework is that it is just so boring I can barely concentrate on it. And it's useless. Who cares whether > means greater than or less than, or what X equals? (Besides, why bother finding out, since X equals something different every time?) The only school thing I like to do is read, and the teachers even take the fun out of that. They don't care that I can almost always solve a mystery before the detective in the story can. They just care that I don't know what an adverb is.

None of this would be so bad if it weren't for Janine. Janine is my sister. She's fifteen and a real-and-true genius. Her I.Q. is 196, which is above average (100), and even above the cutoff point for geniusness, which is 160. Actually, I'll tell you a secret. My I.Q. is also above average. Everyone is amazed, since I can barely spell, but that's why my parents and teachers come down so hard on me. I'm clever, but I'm not a good student. They say if I'd just *Pay Attention* and *Concentrate*, I could do fine in school. But who cares? I'd never live up to Janine.

You have no idea what it's like to have a genius for an older sister (unless, of course, you have one yourself). You can't even say the simplest thing to her. Yesterday morning all I did was go, "Janine, it's cold outside. Mum wants you to close your window before you leave for school," and do you know what she said? She said, "I find it fascinating that in our society we attempt to regulate the temperature of our environment rather than our bodies. It's so much more difficult and it's highly inefficient. Primitive peoples and peoples in various other societies existing today tend towards the mere addition or removal of clothing, while we invite the use of heating units and air conditioners." I didn't even know there was such a word as *peoples*.

Anyway, to get back to that gloomy evening, Dad said I had to do my homework, and he said it was Mimi's turn to help me. I'm supposed to try to do the work on my own, but one of them sits next to me to keep me from daydreaming, to make sure I do each piece completely, to see that I follow directions and things, and to answer questions if I have them. They're not supposed to do the homework *for* me, but sometimes I can get Janine to give me answers. This is because my dumb homework is *so boring* for her, as she tells me at least twice every time she has to help me, that she'll do anything to speed it along. Well, I'm sorry. I'm sorry I'm not up to trigonomulus, or whatever it is she does. We can't all be scholars.

Mimi, my grandmother, is the best person to help me. She's quiet and soft-spoken and endlessly patient. My family is Japanese, and Mimi and my grandfather (who died long before I was born) brought my mother to the United States when Mum was just a little girl. Mum has no accent whatsoever (neither does my father, who also came to the United States as a small child), but Mimi has this pleasant, rolling accent that reminds me of a ship at sea. And she is polite, polite, polite, never speaking a harsh word.

I got out my geography text.

"What do we have between the covers of this book?" asked Mimi, who thinks books are eyes into the hearts and lives of other people (peoples?). She told me once.

"Geography," I replied. "We read chapter three in class today. Now we have to answer the discussion questions at the end of the chapter. . . . Mimi, if they're discussion questions, why aren't we discussing them? How come Mr Miller is making us write them down?"

"I do not know, my Claudia, but if that is the homework, then you must complete it as your teacher wishes."

"I know." Boy, did I know. A few weeks ago, I would have written down one-word answers or skipped the work altogether. Now there was no way out.

I began to write. Mimi looked on, every now and then pointing out a mis-spelled word or suggesting that I check my punctuation. After geography came maths and then English, and at last I was done. I breathed a sigh that was relief mixed with boredom.

"And what are you going to do now, my Claudia?" asked Mimi.

"Get back to *The Phantom of Pine Hill*," I replied, slapping my English text closed. Mimi knows about my Nancy Drew books, but no one else in the family does. Mum and Dad would tell me to read something more grown-up, and Janine would tell me to read

155

something more worthwhile. (*Her* idea of a really good book, something to curl up with in front of a fire, is *Sources of American Social Tradition*, which at this very moment she's devouring as if she were never going to read again.)

"And what is happening in *The Phantom of Pine Hill?*" asked Mimi.

"Ooh, it's really spooky," I began.

"You like to be scared, my Claudia?"

"Well, yes, I do. I mean, when it's just a book, it's fun. Look outside, Mimi. Look at the wind blowing the trees, and the lightning flashing. It's the perfect night to read a mystery."

Mimi smiled. "Spooky. . . . It is almost Hallowe'en," she remarked. "Just a few more weeks."

I nodded. "But I think I'm too old to go trick-or-treating."

"Well, then, you can dress up and help us hand out the goodies. I'm sure that is almost as much fun as tricks-and-treats."

Mimi knows how much I like to dress up. It's very important to me. I think clothes make a statement about the person inside them. Also, since you have to get dressed every day, why not at least make it fun? Traditional clothes look boring and are boring to put on. So I never wear them. I like bright colours and big patterns and funny touches, such as earrings made from feathers. Maybe this is because I'm an artist. I don't know. Today, for instance, I'm wearing purple jeans that stop just below my knees and are held up with braces, white tights with patterns on them, a purple-check shirt with a matching hat, my high-top sneakers, and lobster earrings. Clothes like these are my trademark.

I like costumes, too, and I'll really miss being able to show one off this year. But, as Mimi said, I could make one just to wear when I pass out goodies. Maybe I'll dress up as a Smurf. Blue makeup would be fun.

I stood up. "Thanks for helping me, Mimi. I wish you could help me every night."

"I know, my Claudia, but I think it is better to take turns. Some evenings I am busy, and your mother and father like to see your work, too."

"Right." So why does Janine have to help me? It's because my homework is so boring, no one can stand it for more than one night in a row—even Mimi—and the less often they have to help me, the better (for them).

I was halfway upstairs when I remembered something. I turned around and ran back down to the ground floor. "Mimi?" I called.

"Yes, my Claudia?" She was settling down with a fat book.

"I just thought of something. Let's work on your portrait." In my art class, we'd been given two projects that term. One was the still life, and one was a portrait. Both were to be done in oils. Mimi was the subject of my portrait. "Would you mind?" I asked. "We'll just work for half an hour or so."

"That would be fine." Mimi carefully placed a marker in her book. She followed me to my room.

I know artists are supposed to paint in daylight, but between school and baby-sitting, I didn't have many daylight hours left over. I had to settle for painting in my room with every light blazing.

I posed Mimi in the easy chair, adjusted my easel, and got to work. It was the third time Mimi had sat for me, and the painting was really coming along.

"Mimi?" I said after a few minutes. "Tell me about when you were a little girl in Japan."

Mimi smiled and began the story I'd heard so many times before. She was good at talking without moving round. "We were a family very much like this one," she said. "I lived with my parents, my oldest sister, and my grandfather—my father's father."

"Mimi," I suddenly interrupted, "did you and your sister get along?"

"Oh, yes," replied Mimi. "My sister was my friend, my dear friend. We studied together and played together. I followed her everywhere and tried to do all the things she did. She was very patient with me."

"Why aren't Janine and I friends?" I asked, frowning at the portrait.

"Being friends takes work," replied Mimi quietly. "To be a good friend you must spend time with someone. You must talk to her and try to understand her. That is how you became friends with Kristy and Mary Anne and Stacey."

"But Janine is impossible to talk to," I protested. "And she never has time for me. Well, hardly ever. She helps me with my homework, but that doesn't count."

"And what about you? Do you have time for your sister?"

"Not very often."

"Some day you will be friends," said Mimi.

I went back to her portrait, and she continued her story. Later, when she had left my room, I got the liquorice bootlaces out of my desk and the Nancy Drew book out from under my mattress, where it was hidden, along with a bag of chocolate bars.

I was up to chapter fourteen in *The Phantom*, and it really was very exciting. Even so, as I chewed away at the liquorice, my thoughts began to wander, and they wandered to Trevor Sandbourne.

I lowered the book.

Trevor Sandbourne is the most gorgeous boy in the entire year at Stoneybrook Middle School. And he happens to have the most romantic name in the whole world. Trevor has jet black hair and dark, brooding eyes and freckles on his nose. He walks through the halls looking serious and deep in thought and he writes poetry for *The Literary Voice*, our school's magazine. I never dreamed I would fall in love with a poet. The only problem is that Trevor and I don't have any classes together, so we don't know each other at all. He probably doesn't even know I'm alive.

R-r-r-r-ing! The sound of the phone made me jump. I reached for the receiver, wondering if there was just the teensiest chance that Trevor was on the other end.

"Hello?"

"Hi, Claud. It's me."

"Hi, Stacey."

"What are you doing?"

"Thinking about Trevor Sandbourne. What are you doing?"

"Thinking about Sam Thomas." (Sam Thomas is one of Kristy's older brothers, and Stacey has an Immense Crush on him. Personally, I think he's too old for her. He's in high school.)

I sighed.

Stacey sighed.

"Any Babysitters Club calls?" she asked after a moment.

"Nope."

"Really?"

"Really." The headquarters for the club

160

is my bedroom. This is because I'm the only one of the four of us with a phone in my room. Not only that, I have a private number. The Babysitters Club meets three times a week in my room and if people call during a meeting, they can reach all four of us at once, so they're bound to get a sitter immediately. As Kristy says, "That's the beauty of the club." Of course, people can call us individually at our homes at other times, and a number of club calls come in on my line when we're not meeting. When that happens, I'm supposed to take down all the information about the job, like when it is, how many kids there will be, and how late the parents will be out—details like that. Then I'm supposed to offer the job to all the club members before calling the client back with a sitter. I'll admit that a few times I've forgotten to do this and have taken the job myself on the spot. But I didn't think it was very nice of Stacey to imply that I was job-hogging.

Stacey sighed again.

"Is anything wrong?" I asked her.

"I just wish I knew more people, that's all."

"You will, Stace. Look, you haven't even been here two months yet. It takes time to make friends." Stacey and her parents had moved to Stoneybrook, Connecticut from New York City in August.

"I suppose so," she said.

"Maybe you and I could get together with Kristy and Mary Anne on Saturday. I mean, to do something besides have a club meeting. Are you free on Saturday?"

"I'm always free," said Stacey.

"Oh, come on, you are not. You get lots of baby-sitting jobs, and you go back to New York with your parents all the time."

"That's not the same as having friends."

"So—let's do something on Saturday, okay? I'll call Kristy and Mary Anne."

"All right."

"See you tomorrow, Stace."

" 'Bye."

" 'Bye."

We hung up and I stared out of the window at the rain. It wouldn't be easy finding something Mary Anne's strict father would allow her to do, or something Stacey's strict diet would allow *her* to do, but I was determined that we would get together. I'd talk to Kristy and Mary Anne in school the next day.

I went back to *The Phantom of Pine Hill*.

2nd
CHAPTER

Stacey, Kristy, Mary Anne, and I did get together on Saturday, but we couldn't think of a thing for the four of us to do together. Mary Anne wasn't allowed to ride her bike to the shopping mall. Stacey couldn't eat sweets or ice cream or anything nice. (She has diabetes and has to control very carefully the amount of sugar she takes in each day.) And there was only one film showing in town and Kristy and I had already seen it.

So we sat in Kristy's front garden. We were sprawled all over the place, except for Stacey who was sitting up primly with her legs tucked under her. She wanted to look nice in case Sam should come along or poke his head out the door or something. Mary Anne had the latest edition of *The Stonybrook News* spread open in front of her, but she wasn't reading it. We were very, *very* bored.

"We could go up in the attic and look through that trunk of antique toys that Mum got from Grandma's," Kristy suggested.

Stacey and I rolled our eyes. Even though Kristy and Mary Anne are twelve just like Stacey and I are, they can be very childish. They're not interested in boys or clothes yet, and sometimes they do the weirdest things. Mary Anne still dresses up her stuffed animals. And they even *look* younger than we do. Kristy has long brown hair which she doesn't do much with yet, and big brown eyes which will look great with makeup in a couple of years. She's small for her age. She looks more like a ten-year-old. Mary Anne also has brown eyes and brown hair. Her father makes her wear her hair in plaits. I wonder how long that will go on. And both of them wear ordinary little-girl clothes—kilts and plain blouses and things like that.

Stacey, on the other hand, dresses much the way I do. She's tall and slender and her mother lets her get her blonde hair permed. She looks older than twelve.

"We could try that new cookie pl—" Mary Anne began, then glanced at Stacey and stopped, remembering the diet problem.

"We could rent a film for your video," I said to Stacey.

"Yeah!" said Kristy.

"Yeah!" said Mary Anne.

"The video's broken," said Stacey.

"Oh."

I picked up a bright yellow maple leaf and twirled the stem between my thumb and forefinger. "I'll tell you guys a secret," I said. "Well, Stacey knows about this, but no one else does."

"How come you've already told Stacey?" asked Kristy accusingly.

"I just did, that's all. Okay?"

I saw Kristy and Mary Anne glance at each other and knew what they were thinking—that Stacey and I left them out of things. Well, maybe we did sometimes.

"Do you want to know the secret or not?"

"Yes," said Kristy grudgingly.

"Okay. Well, here it is . . ." I said slowly, trying to drag out the suspense. "I'm in love!"

"Ohh!" said Mary Anne softly.

"You *are*?" cried Kristy at the same time.

"Who with?" asked Mary Anne.

I sighed deeply. "Trevor Sandbourne." I closed my eyes and leaned against the maple tree.

"Trevor Sandbourne?" repeated Kristy.

Mary Anne squinted at me through her reading glasses and pushed one plait behind her shoulder. "Who's he?"

"Only the most gorgeous boy in school."

"I don't think I've heard of him. Is he in our year?"

"Yup. He's a poet," I said. I tried to describe him.

"Oh!" exclaimed Kristy, right in the middle of my description. "I know who you mean. He's really quiet. He's in my maths class. He sits in the row behind me—right next to Alan Gray."

"Oh, you poor thing," I said. "Alan Gray. Ick."

"Yeah," added Mary Anne, sounding pretty disgusted for Mary Anne, which for most people isn't very disgusted at all. Mary Anne lives alone with her father who is really, really strict and over-protective. Because of him, Mary Anne is shy and "held-in", if you know what I mean. Mr Spier thinks that because Mary Anne's mother is dead he has to go overboard with this careful upbringing making Mary Anne super-polite and rather old-fashioned.

"Who's Alan Gray?" asked Stacey, reminding us that she was a newcomer to Stoneybrook.

"Alan Gray," said Kristy witheringly, "is the most disgusting boy in this whole solar system. He's been awful since kindergarten. Probably since birth. And I can tell you it's no picnic having Alan sit right behind me. Yesterday he told Mr Peters that I was late for class because I had to go to the doctor for a flea bath."

"That's *awful*!" exclaimed Stacey.

"I know. He really hates me. He doesn't

166

bother anyone else half as much as he bothers me."

"Well, you *are* the only girl who ever fought him back, you know," I pointed out.

"Yeah," said Kristy with a grin.

A slow smile spread across Mary Anne's face as she remembered what we were talking about. Even Mary Anne had thought it was funny.

"*What*?" demanded Stacey, looking frustrated.

"Two years ago," I began. "That year Kristy, Mary Anne, Alan, and I were all in the same class. Kristy really got Alan. He'd been tormenting us—all the girls, really—for the entire year, and by June we had had it. So one day, Kristy comes to school and all morning she brags about this fantastic lunch her mother had packed: a chocolate cupcake, crisps, fruit salad, a ham and cheese sandwich, two walnut whips—really great stuff. Kristy says it's a reward for something or other. And she says the lunch is so great she's got to protect it by keeping it in her desk instead of in the cloakroom. So, of course, Alan steals the bag out of her desk during the morning. Then at lunchtime in the cafeteria, he makes a big production out of opening it. He's sitting at the boys' table and they're all crowded round and us girls are looking on from the next table. Alan is the centre of attention, which is just what he wants."

"And just what I wanted," added Kristy.

"Right. So Alan carefully takes all the packets and containers out of the bag and spreads them in front of him. Then he begins to open them. In one he finds dead spiders, in another he finds a mud pie."

"David Michael had made it for me," said Kristy. (David Michael is Kristy's little brother. He was four then.)

"She'd even wrapped up a sandwich with fake flies stuck on it."

Stacey began to giggle.

"It was great," said Mary Anne. "Everyone was laughing. And Kristy had packed a real lunch for herself which she'd kept in the cloakroom. All afternoon, the kids kept telling her how terrific her trick had been."

"The only bad thing," said Kristy, "is that ever since, Alan has thought he has to bother me constantly in order to keep up his reputation. He's like the plague."

"Thank goodness Trevor isn't like that," I said.

"If he was, you wouldn't have fallen in love with him," Stacey pointed out. She brushed her curly blonde hair out of her eyes.

"That's true. Poets are sensitive and thoughtful."

We fell silent.

Mary Anne flipped idly through *The Stoneybrook News*. "Taylor's is going to have a sale," she announced.

"Mmm." (I had closed my eyes and was trying to conjure up a picture of Trevor in my mind.)

"There was a fire at the shopping mall this week."

"Mmm."

"Everyone's supposed to get 'flu shots by November."

"Mmm."

"Aughhh!"

Kristy, Stacey, and I jerked to attention.

"What is it? What is it?" we cried.

Mary Anne had turned pale.

With one shaking hand, she pointed at the paper. With the other hand, she held the paper away from her, as if it might bite.

"Is something on the paper?" I shrieked. I jumped away. I absolutely *hate spiders*.

"No, *in* the paper," Mary Anne managed to say.

Kristy grabbed it from her and she and Stacey knelt on the ground and leaned over the pages Mary Anne had it opened to.

" '*Angry Pig Goes Hog Wild*'?" asked Kristy, reading one of the larger headlines.

"No!" cried Mary Anne.

" '*Depressed Trucker Drives Self Crazy*'?" asked Stacey.

"No!"

"What *is* it, Mary Anne? Just tell us," I shouted. "You're driving *us* crazy."

Mary Anne had calmed down a little. She took the paper back and read: " '*Phantom*

169

Caller on Rampage in Mercer.' " She cleared her throat and glanced at us. Then she began to read again. " 'The thief, whom police have nick-named the Phantom Caller, struck again in Mercer on Tuesday night. Following the pattern of his previous burglaries, he began making phone calls, this time to the home of Thornton and Sophia Granville of 236 Witmer Court, shortly after four p.m. He never spoke, simply hanging up the phone when someone answered. The Granvilles left their home at seven-thirty to attend a meeting of the school governors. When they returned at ten-fifteen, they found all of Mrs Granville's jewellery missing. Nothing else had been taken, despite the fact that a considerable amount of silver, as well as Thornton Granville's famous and very valuable coin collection, were in the house.

" 'This is the sixth house the Phantom Caller has robbed in the past two weeks, and the second one in Mercer. The first four robberies occurred in New Hope.' " Mary Anne stopped reading.

"So what is so scary about that?" asked Stacey. "You should hear what goes on in New York City every day."

"But don't you see?" asked Mary Anne. "He's getting closer and closer to Stoneybrook—to *us*. First New Hope, then Mercer. Stoneybrook is the nearest town to Mercer."

"Well, it's still forty kilometres away," I

said. "Does he always steal jewellery?"

"Yes," replied Mary Anne. "Just jewellery. It says in the next paragraph that he really knows what he's looking for. Now here's the scary part: he makes those phone calls to find out whether anyone's home. But *some*times if the people don't go out he robs them anyway, and they don't know it until they realize the jewellery's missing. He's *in* the house while they are. He's never hurt anyone, but what do you think he'd do if he met someone face-to-face in the middle of a burglary? Now think about *this*," she went on. "We don't know what kind of jewellery the people we baby-sit for have."

"Oh," said Stacey, "no one round here is as rich as those Granvilles sound."

"But maybe it doesn't matter," said Kristy. "And what if the Phantom Caller were watching the house or something and saw the parents go out. He might go ahead and rob it if he thought just a baby-sitter and a couple of little kids were there."

"I still don't know," said Stacey. "I think you're worrying about nothing."

Suddenly I clapped my hand to my mouth.

"Oh, gosh!" I cried.

"What?" the others shouted.

"When I baby-sat for the Marshalls on Wednesday, the phone rang twice and each time I answered it, the caller hung up without saying a word!"

171

"Oh, no!"

"You're kidding!"

"I think," said Kristy seriously, "that we should hold an emergency meeting of the Babysitters Club—*now*."

3rd CHAPTER

The members of the Babysitters Club gathered numbly in my bedroom.

"This is *terrible*," moaned Kristy. "How can we baby-sit under these conditions?"

Nobody said a word. To ease the tension, I took a gigantic chocolate bar out of my notebook, carefully peeled back the wrapper, and offered pieces to Kristy and Mary Anne. I didn't even bother to feel bad that Stacey couldn't eat any. The three of us chewed in silence.

"Look," said Stacey after a while, "I think we're worrying about nothing. The Phantom Caller hasn't even robbed anybody in Stoneybrook, so he's still at least forty kilometres away." She turned to Mary Anne. "What makes you so sure he'll come here next? Maybe he'll decide that with the police on his tail he should just clear out and go and rob people in Oklahoma."

"That's true," said Mary Anne slowly.

"And in the second place, if anyone we sit for *does* have some fantastic piece of jewellery and the Phantom Caller has heard about it, don't you think *we'd* have heard about it, too? I mean, it wouldn't be any secret then."

"That's true, too," I said, "but . . . well, what if we just happened to be baby-sitting somewhere and a burglar tried to break in? Not the Phantom Caller necessarily, but any burglar? It could happen, you know, and we should be prepared."

"You're right," said Kristy. "Good baby-sitters should be prepared for anything."

"Maybe," said Stacey, "we should arrange a code we could give each other over the phone that would be a signal for the other person to call the police. Let's say I'm baby-sitting for Jamie Newton, and I hear a burglar. I want to call the police, but I don't want the burglar to *hear* me calling the police, right?"

"Right," said the rest of us.

"So what I do is call Claudia, for example, and I say, 'Hi, it's Stacey. *Have you found my red ribbon*?' and that's a signal that I'm in trouble and need Claudia to call the police."

"Hey, that's a neat idea!" said Kristy.

"Yeah!" agreed Mary Anne. "But how would Claudia know where you are? How would she know where to send the police?"

"That's right. That's a good question, Stace," I said, "because what if the burglar were *listening in on an extension*? I couldn't just say, 'Okay, I'll call the police. Where are you?' That wouldn't do you any good at all."

"Aughh! Listening in on an extension! That is *so* creepy!" screamed Kristy.

"But it could happen," I said. "It happened in that thriller, *The Night of the Weird*. You know, the one where they find the baby-sitter—"

"Stop! Stop! Stop! Don't say any more. I don't want to know!" cried Kristy.

"All right, but the point is," I said, "that we should all know where each one of us is sitting and when."

"Well," said Mary Anne, "there's the record book."

The record book is where we keep track of our baby-sitting appointments as well as all other important club information. Kristy makes us keep a club notebook, too. Each time we complete a job, we're supposed to write about what happened. Then the other club members will know about any problems with children or their families or homes, and know what to expect the next time they sit for the client.

I should mention here that each of us holds an office in the Babysitters Club. Mary Anne is secretary, which is why she was thinking of the record book. Kristy is chairman, since the club was her idea. I'm vice-chairman, since the headquarters is in my bedroom and I have a private phone. And Stacey is treasurer, since she likes numbers.

"What about the record book?" asked Stacey.

"It's got all the information in it—our appointments, the money we've earned, everything. I could bring it to school every day so we could check the calendar. And during our regular Friday meetings we could check it for the weekend. That way each of us would be sure to know what the others are doing—where they're going to be baby-sitting."

"That's a good suggestion," said Kristy, "except that, as chairman, I'll take the responsibility for the book during school. If anything happens to it, it'll be my fault."

"You don't have to do that," I said. "We could take turns."

"No, it's easier if the same person always has it. I don't mind. So I propose that I should bring it to school every day."

"I second that," said Mary Anne, looking relieved.

"Good," said Kristy. "Now what about burglar alarms?"

"What about them?" I countered.

"I think that if we're baby-sitting and anything strange happens—a silent phone call, a funny noise outside, *any*thing—we should rig up some kind of burglar alarm so that at least we'd know if someone tried to break into the house."

For a moment nobody spoke. At last Mary Anne said, "You mean like stacking tins in front of a door so that if the door opened, the tins would crash down and alert you?"

"Exactly!" cried Kristy. "That's a good idea." She tore a piece of paper out of my geography notebook and wrote:

1. Stack tins in front of door or window (inside).

"But," she added, "make sure you don't put them where the children you're sitting for could fall over them. And make sure you put them away before the parents come home."

"Right," we agreed.

"Okay. Other ideas? Claudia?" asked Kristy. She was beginning to sound like some of my teachers.

"No," I said crossly, feeling embarrassed. Then I added, "Do you have any?" realizing that Kristy had been doing a lot of talking and writing and not much thinking.

There was an awkward silence. Then, "How about a Smell Alert?" said Kristy with a giggle.

Mary Anne and Stacey laughed, but I thought Kristy was sounding pretty childish again.

"What," I demanded, "is a Smell Alert, if I may ask?"

Kristy couldn't stop giggling. "You put something really awful, like rubbish, outside the house, where the burglar is bound to step in it. Then when he breaks in, you smell him before you can even hear him. A Smell Alert!"

I had no intention of laughing. All I said was, "You know, a burglar *could* be a woman. It doesn't have to be a man."

"Aw, Claud, it was a *joke*," said Kristy. "Come on."

"Well, I don't *have* any ideas."

"Okay, okay, we'll keep thinking. Now I'm going to write out our code words. You *have* to keep these a secret. Keep the whole page a secret. Nobody should know our code. . . . I'm serious now."

"Okay," we agreed.

"Should we stick with what Stacey said?" added Kristy.

"What did she say? I forget," said Mary Anne.

"She said, '*Have you found my red ribbon?*'" I replied quickly, glad to be able to answer something.

"Yes," said Kristy. "And that means that there's some kind of trouble and the baby-sitter needs the police."

"I think," I said slowly, "that we should stick with what Stacey said, but that we

178

should have a few more code words so we can give more information.

"Yeah. In case there's a burglar listening in on the phone, the person who gets the phone call should answer *in code* to let the baby-sitter know her message was understood and that the friend knows where's she's sitting and so on," added Stacey.

"How about this for the answer?" suggested Mary Anne. "The person would say, 'No, the blue one.' It's simple, and it's still in code."

"That's good," said Kristy, but I could see her shiver at the very thought of a burglar listening in to her conversation.

"I think we should also have a way to let someone know whether we're in really bad trouble," said Stacey, "like if a burglar is in the house and we've actually seen him—or whether we just *think* there's trouble."

"Yeah," I replied. "That's important."

"Okay," said Kristy, "how about this: After the person who gets the call for help goes, 'No, the blue one,' the baby-sitter goes, 'Now I'm in for it,' if it's trouble, or, 'That's okay,' if she's not sure there's trouble?"

"All right," we agreed.

"I hope I can keep all this straight," I said.

"Let's practise," Kristy suggested. "Claudia, let's say you're baby-sitting for David Michael at my house and you hear a noise at the window. What would you do?"

"I'd call Stacey," I said.

"Let's hear your conversation. Remember, you don't know where the burglar is, if there is a burglar, so you have to use the code."

"Okay . . . Okay, I'd pick up the phone and call Stace—"

"*Ring! Ring! Ring!*" said Kristy, imitating the phone.

Stacey placed an imaginary receiver at her ear. "Hello?"

"Hi, Stace. It's Claud. Did you see my ribbon?"

"No. *Have* you *found* my *red* ribbon?" interrupted Kristy.

"No, I haven't," I said.

"*Claud*! Come on, do it right."

"I'm trying . . . Okay. Ring, ring, ring."

"Hello?" said Stacey.

"Hi, it's Claudia. How are you?"

"Not 'How are you'!" cried Kristy. "Get to the point. You're not making a polite call. You're scared to death!"

I sighed. "Hi, Stacey. It's me, Claudia. Have you . . . have you *found* my red ribbon?"

Silence. Then Stacey burst out laughing. "I forgot what I'm supposed to say!"

Kristy looked ready to kill us. "Claud, call Mary Anne instead."

"Okay. Ring, ring."

"Hello?"

180

"Hi, Mary Anne. It's Claudia. Have you found my red ribbon?"

"No, I haven't."

"*No, the blue one!*" shouted Kristy. "Mary Anne, *you* made up this part of the code. You ought to know it."

"I know. I just—I don't know. Start again, Claud."

We practised a bit longer, until we had the code pretty well memorized. Even so, Kristy told us that when we each had a copy of the code words, we should read them once a day to make sure we didn't forget them. She is bossy sometimes.

Later, as the girls were getting ready to leave the room, Mary Anne suddenly clapped her hand over her mouth. "Oh, no!" she exclaimed.

"What is it?" I asked.

"I've just thought of something. What if my father hears about the Phantom Caller? I bet he won't let me baby-sit any more."

"But we decided we don't have to worry about the Phantom Caller," I pointed out.

"I know, but if Dad finds out about our code words, forget it. It'll give him something to worry about. I don't think he's thought of robbers and things."

"Maybe we should keep *all* this a secret from *all* our parents," said Kristy. "You know how parents are. Mary Anne's right. They're always worrying. Let's just go on as if we never thought of any of these things today. Agreed?"

"Agreed!"

The emergency meeting of the Babysitters Club was over. But our adventure was just beginning.

4th CHAPTER

There he is! I told myself excitedly. A Trevor-sighting was always a big event.

I was dodging through the halls of Stoneybrook Middle School trying to remain a safe distance behind Trevor Sandbourne without losing sight of him. It was eight o'clock. The first bell would ring in exactly two minutes.

Trevor came to a sudden stop outside the door to the office of *The Literary Voice*. I stopped, too, and someone ran into me from behind. *Crash!* We fell against some lockers. I turned round. I was face-to-face with Alan Gray.

"Watch where you're going!" I said. I straightened my bow tie with the little Scottie dogs on it, and patted my hair to see if any damage had been done. My hair is long and I can do lots of things with it. That day I had fixed it in five slim plaits and looped each one up on my head, holding them in place with beaded slides that had sparkly streamers attached to them.

"*Me*! What about you?" said Alan as he straightened his books. Then he stalked off, saying in a soft singsong voice, "Claud and Trevor sitting in a tree, K-I-S-S-I-N-G."

Oh, he makes me mad! And how did he know about my crush on Trevor, anyway? Someone must have let the cat out of the bag, and I had a good idea who that someone was.

The bell rang then and I had to run all the way to my classroom. I sat through the register and the morning announcements thinking of Trevor. I had this daydream about us.

Our year is being taken on a field trip to visit the colonial Bradford Mansion in Wutherby. We're split into groups and Trevor and I are in the same group. After we tour the house, we go out back to the gardens and start wandering through the giant maze made of yew hedges. Trevor and I reach a dead end together and are just about to turn round when we realize it's snowing, even though it's June.

"Hey, what's that?" says Trevor. He points to a little wooden door hidden in the bushes.

"I don't know," I reply. "Let's see. Maybe we can get out of the snow for a while."

184

We open the door and find ourselves in another world. The snow is gone, and so are the maze, the Bradford Mansion, and the other kids. We're no longer in Wutherby. For all I know, we're not even on Earth. Maybe we're in the fourth dimension. It doesn't matter. Wherever we are, we're alone together. . . .

"Claudia?"

I shook myself awake. Darn. I have never been able to finish that daydream. If my teachers would just leave me alone, I could find out what happens.

"Yes?" I was in a maths class. It was the third time that morning that I'd started the dream.

"May I have your homework, please?" Our teacher, Mr Peters, was peering at me with great concern. Most of my teachers look at me that way.

"Oh. Of course." I got my homework paper out of my notebook and placed it on the pile. I knew it was all correct because Janine had been my helper for my weekend homework, and she was a real stickler for the maths problems, as you can probably imagine.

"Claudia, Claudia," she was always saying, with as much concern as my teachers. "You're confusing *whole* numbers with *even* numbers. A whole number can be even *or* odd, just as long as it's a negative or positive *integer*."

Well, that certainly cleared things up. Why can't Janine talk to me like a normal person? When we were little, she used to be normal. We could play together and have fun. She even seemed to have some sort of an imagination, although that's hard to believe now.

Maths class ended and I headed slowly for English. I've been dreading English for the last couple of weeks because of this book we're reading. It's called *The Pond* and I'll be honest with you, I just don't get it. It's not that I don't understand the words; I know all the vocabulary. It's just that I'm not getting much out of it except that this kid goes squirrel-hunting a lot. I'm sure there's more to the story than that—some kind of message—but I don't know what it is. Furthermore, I don't care. Maybe if I didn't try to read it so *fast*. . . .

School is absolutely a complicated mess. Give me Nancy Drew any day.

In English we had to read aloud from *The Pond*. The teacher told me to read with more feeling. Then she handed back these vocabulary quizzes we'd had the week before. I got a seventy. That was not going to please anybody in my family. It didn't please *me*. I know that you spell *October* O-C-T-O-B-E-R, but I'd written O-C-O-B-E-R. *Pay attention, Claudia.*

I was very glad to get to the cafeteria for lunch.

"Stacey!" I called. I'd spotted her ahead of me in the hot-lunch queue. "Save me a seat at our table, okay?"

She nodded.

Ordinarily, I might have tried to sneak into the queue with her, but she was standing next to this kid, Alexander Kurtzman, who carries a briefcase and wears a jacket and tie, and *lives* to obey rules. One of his favourites is "No queue-jumping," so there was really no point in trying to butt in.

I looked round the cafeteria and saw Kristy and Mary Anne eating with three other girls—Lauren Hoffman and the Shillaber twins, Mariah and Miranda. The Shillaber twins, who are identical, were dressed alike. I couldn't believe it. They are too old for that, I think. But then, Kristy and her friends *can* be babyish. They had even brought packed-lunches that day because the hot lunch was chicken fricassee, which I admit is on the disgusting side. However, it's embarrassing to bring your lunch to school in our year. For one thing, it gives your locker a permanent smell of sandwiches.

I reminded myself that I needed to have a little talk with Miss Kristy Thomas.

I got my chicken fricassee and sat down with Stacey. Pretty soon we were joined by Dorianne Wallingford (talk about romantic names), Emily Bernstein, Howie Johnson,

Pete Black, and Rick Chow. We were all eating the chicken, and the boys had eight desserts between them. They pack away more food at every meal than a football team does.

"Do you guys think you have enough food?" I asked, as I opened my milk carton and arranged the things on my tray.

"Enough for a food sculpture," replied Pete.

"Oh, no! Not today!" I exclaimed with a giggle. The boys had been bringing toothpicks to school and using their milk cartons and rubbish to make food creations. Once they made Mrs Pinelli, the music teacher. They gave her spaghetti hair, grape eyes, and an apple head. We got yelled at for wasting food.

Dorianne ignored the boys. She nibbled at her chicken and looked tragic. She can be very dramatic sometimes.

"What is it?" I asked her finally.

Dorianne sighed loudly. The boys stopped gobbling up their food, and looked at her. "We were robbed last night," she said. I dropped my fork with a clatter and almost choked on a mouthful of carrots. "You *were*?"

"Well . . . not *us* exactly."

"Who exactly?"

"Nana and Gramps. And it looks like the work of . . . the Phantom Caller!"

I think my heart actually stopped beating

for a few moments.

"The Phantom Caller?" I squeaked.

Dorianne nodded her head tragically.

"Wh-where do your grandparents live?" I asked, dreading her answer.

"In New Hope." Dorianne allowed a tiny bit of chicken to enter her mouth.

I let out a sigh of relief. So the caller was back in New Hope. "Oh, *well*," I said. "In *New* Hope. That's okay."

"Claudia, what are you talking about? He got Nana's sapphire and diamond engagement ring and her diamond choker."

"I'm sorry, Dor," I said. "I didn't mean . . . It's just that, well, it's better than if he were robbing houses here in Stoneybrook, isn't it?"

Dorianne gave me a funny look. "I guess."

Splat! The boys had lost interest in our conversation and had started a food sculpture. Half a banana had just fallen off a tower of milk cartons and landed in Emily's chicken. The chicken splashed onto her mohair sweater.

"Ew, ew!" she cried. "Rick! Look what you did! My sister is going to kill me!"

"Why is your sister going to kill you?" he asked.

"Because this is her sweater."

"Oh. Sorry."

"Come on, Emily," I said. "Let's go to the cloakroom. I'll help you to wash it off."

"All right."

As I stood in the cloakroom sponging off Emily's front with damp paper towels, Emily leaned forward and whispered, "So, what is this about you and Trevor Sandbourne?"

My heart stopped beating again. If that kept up, I wouldn't live to see thirteen. I checked the cubicles to make sure we were alone. "Nothing," I said. "And what did you hear?"

"That you like him."

"Who'd you hear it from?"

"Dorianne."

"Who'd she hear it from?"

Emily shrugged. "I don't know."

"Well, I know something. I know that Kristy Thomas has a big, fat mouth."

"Kristy!" exclaimed Emily. "What does she care about stuff like this?"

"She cares." But Emily's words made me think. This *wasn't* the kind of thing Kristy cared about. . . . But she *was* a blabbermouth. I threw away the paper towels. "There," I said to Emily. "I think the spots are gone."

"Thanks, Claud."

As we walked out into the hall, we ran into Kristy and Mary Anne. "Thanks for nothing!" I said to Kristy.

"What's that supposed to mean?"

Emily raised an eyebrow at us and disappeared into the cafeteria.

190

"You told about Tr—" I realized I was almost yelling, so I lowered my voice to a whisper. "—about Trevor."

"I did not!" Kristy whispered back.

"Well, everyone seems to know about us. Even Alan Gray."

"Why would I speak to *Alan Gray*?" hissed Kristy.

I paused. "Beats me."

"Beats me, too."

Suddenly I felt awful. "I'm sorry, Kristy. I just can't understand how everyone knows about this."

"Who else did you tell?" asked Mary Anne.

"Just you two and Stacey."

"Well, *I* didn't say anything."

"And I don't think Stacey would."

"It's a mystery," said Kristy.

"Yeah." A mystery. I liked the sound of that. But I still didn't like everyone knowing my private business. "I'm sorry," I said again. "Look, I'll see you two at the meeting this afternoon, okay?" The Babysitters Club meets on Mondays, Wednesdays, and Fridays from five-thirty to six o'clock to take phone calls from clients.

"Okay." Kristy and Mary Anne disappeared into the cloakroom.

I went back to the cafeteria.

Two good things happened that day. The first, of course, had been the Trevor-sighting in the morning. The second happened just before the final bell rang, when Mr Taylor, the headmaster, came over the intercom with the afternoon announcements.

He reminded us about having our school pictures taken and about some club meetings. Then he said, "On Friday, October thirty-first—that's Hallowe'en, children"—duh—"our first school dance, the Hallowe'en Hop, will take place. It will be held in the main gymnasium from four o'clock until six o'clock. Costumes are not required, but they're welcome. We hope to see all of you there. By the way, the dance committee will have a fifteen-minute meeting in my office straight after the last bell. That's all. Good afternoon."

I sighed dreamily. The Hallowe'en Hop. Would Trevor go? More important, would he ask me to go? Well, he might—but not if he didn't know who I was. That would be crucial to getting an invitation. I sighed again. The second sigh was hopeless. After all, Trevor didn't even know I was alive.

5th CHAPTER

"Hi-hi!" Jamie Newton flung open his front door and greeted me happily. Jamie is three years old. Kristy and I are his favourite baby-sitters. Jamie is always glad to see us.

"Hi!" I said. "Are you ready to play?"

"Yup!"

Mrs Newton appeared in the doorway behind Jamie. "Hello, Claudia," she said. "You're right on time." She held the door open for me, and I walked in and followed Mrs Newton to the kitchen.

Mrs Newton is one of my favourite people in the whole world. She never asks me about school, but she always asks me about my art and tells me she likes what I'm wearing. Mrs Newton is pregnant. Jamie is going to have a little brother or sister soon. Very soon. Mrs Newton is so big she looks as if she should fall over forward instead of standing up straight.

"Oh, Claudia," she said, "what wonderful slides! Where did you get them?"

My slides were teddy bears with streamers attached. "At The Merry-Go-Round," I replied. "Three dollars and seventy-five cents."

"Hmm. Maybe I'll get a pair. Not for me, of course. For the baby. I'm sort of hoping for a G-I-R-L."

I smiled.

"I have to spell that," she added, "because Jamie wants a B-O-Y. How are your art classes? What are you working at now?"

"Two oil paints. We've just started using oils. I'm doing a portrait of Mimi and a still life."

"What's in the still life?"

"An egg, a check napkin, a wooden spoon, and a jug."

"An egg! That must be difficult."

"Yeah, it is. But I like working at it."

Mrs Newton checked her watch. "I'd better get going," she said. "I'll be at the doctor's first for a quick checkup, then I just have to stop at the post office and the grocer's. I'll be home by five o'clock, maybe a bit earlier. You know where the phone numbers are."

"Of course," I said. "Jamie and I are going to have fun. Do you want to play outside, Jamie?" It was a grey, dreary day, but it wasn't raining.

"Yeah!"

I was glad he did, because I was just a little afraid of the Phantom Caller. I knew he usually struck after dark, and I knew he hadn't robbed anyone in Stoneybrook— yet—but I was still scared.

Mrs Newton left, and I put Jamie's jacket on him. We went into his back garden. The Newtons' garden is really good for little children to play in. There's a slide and a swing set and a jungle gym, and the garden is completely surrounded by a tall wooden fence.

I pushed Jamie on the swing for a while. Then he jumped off and ran to the jungle gym to show me a trick he'd learned. I was facing the house, watching him, when I saw something that nearly made me jump out of my skin.

A light came on downstairs in the Newtons' house. It lit up the living room, but it didn't look like a living room light. Maybe it was in the front hall.

A chill ran up my spine.

I looked at my watch. Four o'clock. Mrs Newton should have been with the doctor just then. Besides, if she'd come back, I would have heard her car pull up and the door slam.

As I stared at the house, the light went off.

I gasped.

Maybe it was some kind of illusion—like

a street light. But why would a street light turn on and then go off?

I decided to ignore the light.

Jamie stood up on the bottom of his slide. "Hey, guess who I am!" he yelled. He beat his chest and cried, "Ah! Ah-ah-ah-ah!"

"Peter Rabbit?" I said.

Jamie laughed. "No!"

"Superman?"

"No!"

"Not Tarzan?" I said.

"Yes! I'm Tarzan."

At that moment, the phone began to ring. I looked at the house.

"I hear the telephone," said Jamie. "Maybe it's Daddy."

I'd been hoping he wouldn't hear it. I hadn't intended to answer it.

Jamie ran for the house. "Come on!" he said.

I knew I should answer the phone. As a baby-sitter, that was one of my responsibilities. But I was too afraid. I stooped down. "Just a second," I called. "My shoe's untied." I took long enough untying and retying my sneaker so that by the time I caught up with Jamie at the back door, the phone was no longer ringing. "I'm sorry, Jamie," I said. "Look, if it was your dad, he'll call back."

"Okay." Jamie didn't seem too upset. He sat down on the patio and began playing with a dump truck. "Beep, beep! Beep,

beep! . . . Hey, what was that?" he asked, standing still.

"What was what?"

"That noise."

"What noise?"

Pat, pat, pat.

"*That* noise."

I had heard it, too. Footsteps on the driveway, on the other side of the wooden fence.

I didn't know what to do. I was afraid to take Jamie into the house, but the only way to leave the Newtons' garden was through the gate in the fence. And the gate opened onto the drive.

"Maybe it was the paperboy," I suggested.

Jamie shook his head. "The paperboy doesn't come up to our house. He stands in the street and throws the paper into the flower garden."

Pat, pat, pat.

"Hey," I whispered, "let's be spies. Let's sneak up to the fence and peek through the knothole by the gate."

"Okay," Jamie whispered back.

I took Jamie's hand and we tiptoed across the grass to the gate. Very cautiously, I closed one eye and put the other one up to the hole.

A brown eye was looking back at me!

I screamed.

Jamie screamed.

197

The person attached to the brown eye screamed.

That last scream sounded awfully familiar. "Kristy?" I said.

"Claudia?" The gate opened and Kristy came in, trembling.

"*What were you doing*?" I shouted.

"Trying to find you," she said. "Hi, Jamie."

"Hi-hi."

"I thought you were the—PC," I said, nodding toward Jamie.

"Sorry. Mum got home from work early today, so I'm off the hook with David Michael." (Kristy and her elder brothers each have to take care of their littlest brother, David Michael, one afternoon a week while Mrs Thomas is at work. A baby-sitter comes on the other days.) "I knew you were baby-sitting here," she went on. "Mum sent me over with something for Mrs Newton and I wanted to see how you you were doing. I was sort of worried about the—PC myself."

"Did you turn on the light in the Newtons' house?"

Kristy nodded. "Mum made a casserole for the Newtons since Mrs Newton doesn't feel much like cooking any more. I had to put on a light so I wouldn't trip with it on my way to the refrigerator. Then I went back outside to look for you two."

"I suppose that wasn't you on the phone

198

then," I said.

Kristy's eyes opened wide. "The phone rang?"

"Just a couple of minutes ago, while you were walking round looking for us."

"Did you answer it?"

"No, we—I missed it."

"I bet it was Daddy," said Jamie.

Kristy and I exchanged knowing looks.

"Do you want me to stay for a while?" asked Kristy.

"Yes!" said Jamie and I, for different reasons.

Kristy can be a blabbermouth and a baby, but she can also be a very good friend.

6th CHAPTER

That night, Janine helped me with my homework. She is fussy, fussy, fussy. I bet teachers wouldn't even notice half the things she makes me correct. We were just finishing when a great crash of thunder sounded.

"Gosh, it's late in the season for thunderstorms," Janine remarked.

"Ooh, but I love them," I said. "They make me feel all shivery. . . . Janine?"

"Hmmm?"

"Remember when we were little and we'd crawl under Mum and Dad's bed during thunderstorms? We'd pretend we were camping—"

"But we were really just hiding."

"Yeah," I said fondly.

"Very interesting, psychologically," said Janine. "The fear process—"

"Janine?"

"What?"

"Shut up."

Janine glared at me, then stalked out of the room. I knew Mimi had said I would have to work at being Janine's friend, and she was right. It would take a *lot* of work. How did Janine get the "fear process" out of something as nice as autumn thunderstorms? Even so, I resolved not to give up so easily the next time we talked.

I flicked on the radio and tuned it to the local station. I listened to it while I worked on my still life. Maybe the weather forecast would mention something about the thunderstorm.

I dabbed away at the grey area under the egg. It's hard to work out what shape shadow an egg will cast.

The music came to an end and I pricked up my ears. "At the top of the news," said the radio newscaster suddenly, "is a local story. The thief dubbed the Phantom Caller has been spotted in a stolen car, travelling south through New Jersey. State police are tailing him. Details in our next bulletin."

"All right!" I cried. "He's gone!" I was so excited that I turned off the radio, snatched up the phone, and called Stacey. "Guess what! Guess what," I cried.

"What?" said Stacey excitedly. "Wait. Trevor called you. Oh, I knew he would. I *knew* it! Oh, Claud, did he ask—"

"Stacey, Stacey," I said. "That's not it."

I felt like a deflated balloon. "He didn't call. It's something else." Unfortunately, the something else wasn't as exciting as Trevor.

"Oh," said Stacey.

"The Phantom Caller's gone. I've just heard it on the radio."

"You're kidding."

"Nope. Heading south through New Jersey. Away from us. The police are after him."

"Oh, I hope they catch him."

"Well, even if they don't, he's out of our hair. We can forget about the Phantom Caller for good."

A little while later, I hung up the phone. Then I called Kristy to tell her the news, and then I called Mary Anne.

Boy, were we relieved.

The next evening I had a sitting job for two little girls, Nina and Eleanor Marshall. On school nights I'm allowed to baby-sit until nine-thirty. The deal with my homework is that I must get it done in the afternoon. I worked at it with my mother.

At seven-thirty that night, I was in the Marshalls' kitchen, pouring a glass of milk for Nina, who's three. (Eleanor, who's just a year old, was already in bed.) The radio was playing in the background. Nina was watching TV in the den.

Then, just like the night before, a song ended, and the announcer began the evening

news with a piece about the Phantom.

Oh, good! I thought. They've captured him.

But I was wrong. Very wrong.

"The man thought to be the Phantom Caller," said the newscaster, "has been captured—and is not the Phantom. The Phantom Caller is still at large."

Still at large! What a horrible way to phrase that. It sounded as if he might be anywhere . . . maybe in the Marshalls' backyard . . . or peering through the kitchen window.

I turned off the radio.

Then I dared to look around to see whether the Phantom Caller was at the window. All I could see were the kitchen lights reflected in the glass.

I put the carton of milk in the refrigerator and picked up the glass. "Nina!" I called. "Here's your milk."

She scurried into the kitchen just as the phone rang. "I want to talk," she said.

I was trembling, but I tried not to let Nina know. "Only if it's your mum," I told her. I picked her up, and lifted the receiver, dreading the voice I might hear, hoping it really was Mrs Marshall just calling to check on things.

"Hello?" I said lightly (for Mrs Marshall's benefit).

Silence.

"Hello? . . . *Hello*?"

More silence. Then a click as the caller hung up.

Oh, my gosh. The Phantom Caller was in Stoneybrook. I just knew it.

I wondered if I should call Stacey and give her our coded message. What was I supposed to ask about? Slides? Ribbons?

"Claudia?"

I jumped a mile as Nina asked, "Who is it?"

"Wrong number," I said. I hung up the phone, put her down, and handed her the milk. "Well, let's go and watch TV," I suggested.

"I can't any more."

"Why not?"

"Because *The Muppet Show* is over. I have to go to bed." Nina was getting a milk moustache.

"So soon?"

"That's my bedtime. After *The Muppet Show*."

I knew when her bedtime was, but maybe just once she could stay up a little longer. "How about a special treat?" I said excitedly. "You can stay up until eight o'clock."

"But Mummy and Daddy don't let me. That's the rule."

What was I doing, anyway, trying to arrange a three-year-old to keep me company? "Okay, then. Upstairs we go."

Nina handed me her empty glass. I put it

in the sink and we climbed the stairs. I turned on every light I could possibly find. I wondered what kind of jewellery Mrs Marshall had.

After Nina was in bed, I tiptoed to Eleanor's room to check on her. I stood in the doorway and let the light from the hall shine into her bedroom. I stared at her cot.

It looked empty!

Oh, gosh! Maybe the Phantom Caller was in the Marshalls' house somewhere and he'd taken Eleanor! I dashed over to her cot. There she was, all bunched into a corner. I straightened her out and covered her up again.

Eleanor sighed in her sleep.

I sighed, too.

I turned off the upstairs lights and went back down to the den. I turned the TV on. Then I turned it off. If the TV was on, the Phantom Caller could sneak up on me too easily. I sat in silence and flipped through a magazine.

Crick, crick, crick.

What was that?

Just the Marshalls' cat settling down on a pile of newspapers.

Plink, plink.

What was that?

Water dripping in the sink.

All the little noises were driving me crazy. I put the TV back on. I tried to watch it, but my gaze kept travelling to the dark windows that faced the back garden. Finally, I couldn't stand it any longer. I shut the curtains.

Then I decided to call Stacey.

"Claudia!" Stacey exclaimed when she got on the phone. "Have you been listening to the news?"

"Yes!" I said. "What do you think?"

"I was just going to call you because I know you're baby-sitting. I don't know *what* to think!"

"Oh, it's so spooky here. Every little noise makes me jump. And you know what? The phone rang a while ago, and *the caller didn't say a word*. He just hung up."

"Oooh. But you're . . . you're not asking about your hair ribbons," Stacey said cautiously.

"No," I replied. "Not yet."

"Do you want me to come over?"

"I do, but I don't want the Marshalls to come home and find you here with me. I don't want them to think I can't handle a simple job by myself."

"Well, do you want to stay on the phone for a while?"

"Yes. That would be great." I decided I didn't care whether Mrs Marshall was trying to call.

"So what's going on with Trevor?" asked Stacey.

"Oh, the usual."

"Nothing?"

"Yeah. I wonder if he even knows about the Hallowe'en Hop. Poets are sometimes off in their own worlds. Maybe he hasn't heard the announcements in school."

"Oh, I bet he has," said Stacey. "How could anyone miss them?" She put her hand over the receiver to disguise her voice and did a pretty good imitation of Mr Taylor talking on the intercom. "As you know, children, Hallowe'en falls on October the thirty-first this year."

I giggled. "Taylor is so dumb. He thinks we—" I broke off.

"Claudia?" asked Stacey.

"Shh." I held the phone away from my ear and listened intently. I definitely heard footsteps in the garage. "Stacey, Stacey," I said urgently. "Have you found my b—I mean, did you see my—Have you found my . . . my . . ."

"Your red ribbon?" whispered Stacey.

"Yes!" I gasped.

"Yes, I did. I mean, no, I found—I. . . ."

"Did you find my blue—Oh, no. Stacey, someone's at the garage door. I can hear the knob rattling!"

"I'm going to call the police."

"Claudia?" called a deep voice.

It was all I could do not to shriek. "He called my name!" I yelped at Stacey.

"Claudia," said the voice again, "we've misplaced the house keys. Can you let us in, please?"

I let my breath out in one long, shaking sigh. "It's the Marshalls, Stace," I whispered. "Gotta go. I'll call you when I get home."

I ran to the back door, unlocked it, and flung it open. I have never, ever, in my whole life, been so glad to see anybody.

'Hi, Claudia," said Mrs Marshall.

Mr Marshall was standing behind her, patting his pockets, and muttering, "I can't understand where those darned keys went."

I held the door open for them. "Sorry for the confusion," Mrs Marshall went on. "The house keys may be at Mr Marshall's office. Here, dear, use mine," said Mrs Marshall to her husband. She took a ring of keys from a peg in the back hall and handed it to him. Then she turned to me. "How were the girls tonight?"

"Oh, just fine," I said. "Nina went to bed as soon as *The Muppet Show* was over."

"Good. No problems, then?"

"None at all." I was still shaking.

Mrs Marshall began rummaging through her handbag for money.

A few minutes later, as Mr Marshall was opening the door to walk me home, the phone rang. I heard Mrs Marshall pick it up and say hello. Then I heard her hang up, saying, "That's strange."

I shivered. It was strange all right.

7th
CHAPTER

Thursday. October 23

This evening I baby-sat at Watson's. It's hard to believe Watson will become my stepfather next year. Oh, well.

As I promised the rest of the club members last Saturday, I've been bringing our club record book to school every day so each of us can check the appointments and see where the others will be baby-sitting. After tonight, I'm not so sure that's a good idea. Karen, Watson's five-year-old daughter, was so nervous about the woman next door who she thinks is a witch, that she was making me nervous. Then, just when I was about the most scared I've ever been, the phone started ringing ... and ringing ... and ringing ...

Poor Kristy, I'm glad she and Watson, her mother's boyfriend, finally get along better. But I suppose it is a little frightening to sit at his house. I've never done it, but Mary Anne has. She was scared, too. And that was a while ago, before we knew anything about the Phantom Caller. To start with, Watson's house is huge, practically a mansion, and the house next door, which is also huge, is gloomy and rambling, with turrets and towers and dark windows everywhere. If that weren't bad enough, little Karen is convinced that Mrs Porter, who lives there, is a witch named Morbidda Destiny who has put two spells on Boo-Boo, Watson's fat cat. On the night Kristy was baby-sitting, Karen had a new twist on her fears about Mrs Porter.

Kristy arrived at Watson's at seven. She can't baby-sit very late on week nights, but Watson was only going to Parents' Night at Karen's private school, so he was going to be home early. Usually his kids, Karen and Andrew, don't stay with him during the week, but since his ex-wife had broken her ankle, Watson was taking them more often than usual.

"Hi, Kristy!" Karen cried, when Mrs Thomas dropped Kristy off at Watson's.

"Hi!" added Andrew happily. Andrew is three.

Andrew and Karen like Kristy so much that not long ago, Kristy promised them she'd be their main baby-sitter at Watson's until she becomes their stepsister.

Watson walked into the front hall. "Well, Kristy," he said warmly, "I'm so glad you could come." (Kristy knew that Watson was really just glad she wasn't such a pill about him and her mother any more.) "I don't think you'll have any trouble tonight."

Kristy smiled at Watson as Boo-Boo wandered into the hall. "I know one way to avoid trouble," she said. "We'll keep Boo-Boo inside." She turned to Karen and grinned at her, but Karen just stared back solemnly. Uh-oh, thought Kristy. Something's wrong.

"All right," said Watson, "the emergency numbers are in the usual place, and the phone number of Karen's school is taped to the phone, just in case." Kristy nodded. "Seven-thirty-bedtime for Andrew," Watson went on, "and eight o'clock for Karen. By the way, there's peppermint ice cream in the freezer and . . . I don't believe Andrew and Karen have had dessert yet."

"Yea! Ice cream!" cried Andrew, jumping up and down.

Karen continued to look solemn.

Kristy began to feel suspicious—and a little nervous.

Watson shrugged into his coat. "Goodbye, darling," he said, kissing the top of Karen's head. "Goodbye, Andy."

He left quickly, calling over his shoulder,

"I'll be home before nine, Kristy. Thanks again."

Kristy glanced warily at Andrew and Karen. This was the moment when even the most baby-sat-for-children sometimes burst into tears. Jamie Newton, for instance, absolutely hated his parents to leave him just before bedtime. But Andrew was already on his way into the kitchen after the ice cream. Karen, apparently, had other things on her mind.

"What's the matter?" Kristy finally asked her, taking her hand. She really didn't want to know, yet it was her job to know.

"Morbidda Destiny," whispered Karen.

"What about her?" Kristy whispered back, a little shivery tickle running up her spine. She remembered how strangely Mary Anne said Boo-Boo had acted the day she was baby-sitting, when Mrs Porter had chased him out of her garden with a rake.

"Kristy? Ice cream?" called Andrew from the kitchen.

"Just a sec, Andrew."

"More spells," whispered Karen urgently.

"Really?" asked Kristy, trying to sound unconcerned. "Boo-Boo looks all right."

"Not Boo-Boo. Me," said Karen. She closed her eyes dramatically.

"You!" exclaimed Kristy. "What's she done to you?"

"Given me freckles."

"Karen," said Kristy, hiding a smile, "you had freckles already. You've had freckles since you were two years old. I've seen pictures."

"She's given me more."

"Sometimes they spread."

Karen shook her head.

"Kristy!" called Andrew, sounding impatient.

"Coming! Karen, I really don't think you need to worry. Let's go and have some ice cream with Andrew, okay?"

"Okay . . . but I'm warning you. If she squints her eyes and holds one hand in the air, she's putting a spell on you."

"I'll be on the alert," Kristy said.

They walked into the kitchen—and found pink ice cream dripping all over the table and onto the floor. Three bowls and three spoons were sitting stickily in the middle of the mess.

"Andrew!" cried Kristy.

"I helped," he said proudly. "I let Boo-Boo out, too."

Kristy turned pale. "You—you let *Boo-Boo* out? Andrew, I—"

"I think he wasn't paying attention," said Karen quickly.

Kristy calmed down. "I suppose not . . . Andrew, thank you very much for helping. But from now on, maybe you should tell me before you help with Boo-Boo, okay? Sometimes we don't let him outside."

Andrew's face fell.

"But," Kristy rushed on, "you did a good job with the ice cream. Thank you. Let's just wipe up the drips and then we can eat it."

Kristy, Karen, and Andrew finished their ice cream. Then Kristy put Andrew to bed and helped Karen change into her pyjamas.

"Let's read stories until my bedtime," Karen suggested.

"Okay," said Kristy. "You choose."

Karen searched through the shelf in her room, then sat down on her bed. Kristy sat next to her. Karen handed her a book.

"What's this?" exclaimed Kristy. "*The Witch Next Door*? Where did this come from?"

"It just appeared," said Karen mysteriously.

Kristy looked at her suspiciously. "Are you sure?"

"Well . . . it appeared from inside Daddy's briefcase. He bought it for me."

"Aha!" said Kristy. "Listen, tonight we're going to read something funny." She took a fat book from the shelf. "Has your daddy read this to you?"

Karen shook her head. "It's too long."

"Not if you read it a little at a time, and that's what we're going to do. Every time I baby-sit, we'll read some more."

"Okay," agreed Karen. She settled herself against her pillow.

"Now," said Kristy, "this story is all about a girl exactly your age whose name is Ramona Quimby."

"Goody," said Karen. "I like that name."

Kristy began to read. Half an hour later, Karen was asleep. Kristy tiptoed downstairs. As soon as she reached the kitchen, the phone rang. Kristy practically jumped out of her skin.

The caller was Mary Anne. "Just checking," she said. "I wanted to see how you're doing."

"Fine," Kristy replied. "Karen and Andrew are in bed. But Karen thinks Mrs Porter has put a freckle-spell on her." Kristy giggled nervously.

"You know," said Mary Anne, "I'd be able to laugh, too, if only Mrs Porter didn't look so . . . so . . ."

"So much like a witch?"

"Well, yes, I mean, she goes flapping around her yard in those horrible black robes like some kind of overgrown bat—"

"Mary Anne, stop!"

"Okay. I'm sorry. Look, I'm not supposed to be on the phone at all. I had to tell Dad this was a homework emergency. I'm glad everything's okay."

"Thanks."

"Lock up tight."

"What?"

"The windows. The doors. Lock them.

Lock everything—just in case."

"All right."

Kristy and Mary Anne hung up and Kristy started walking through Watson's huge, silent house. All the windows seemed to be locked, but Kristy checked each one anyway. The only problem was that there were so many of them. And the locks on some were hard to reach. Kristy was perched precariously on top of a stepladder in the library when the phone rang again.

"Aughh!" Kristy stumbled down the ladder. She reached for the phone on the big leather desktop. Then she drew her hand back, afraid. After three rings, she told herself it was probably just Mary Anne calling back, even though she knew that was unlikely. Mr Spier is *so* strict about letting his daughter talk on the phone after dinner.

"Hello?" said Kristy timidly. ". . . Hello?"

She thought she could hear light breathing on the other end of the phone.

"Hello?" Nothing. Kristy dropped the receiver into the cradle as if it were burning her hand. She ran from the library. She knew she should check the upstairs windows, but she was too afraid. I just know the Phantom Caller is going to sneak onto the first floor, she told herself. He's probably leaning a ladder against the outside of the house at this very moment. He's—

Ring! The phone rang again.

216

Ring . . . Ring.

At first Kristy reached for it. She knew she had to answer it. The caller could be Watson or her mother. She picked up the receiver and held it to her ear. But she couldn't get any words out.

"Kristy?" asked the caller.

"Claudia?" she whispered back. (The caller was me!)

"What's wrong?" I asked her.

"I just got one of those calls."

"Oooh."

"And Watson's house is so huge and scary."

"Put on lots of lights," I suggested.

"What do you think the calls mean?" Kristy asked. She couldn't stop thinking about them. I knew just how she felt.

"Well," I said, "they could be wrong numbers. People are pretty rude when they reach the wrong person. They usually just hang up. Or they could be little children making stupid calls."

"I suppose so," said Kristy.

"In case there's any trouble, do you remember our code?"

"No."

"Kristy! You were the one who made us rehearse. Where's your sheet with the code words?"

"At home. I didn't know how it would feel to be so nervous. I can't even remember my last name."

"It's Thomas."

"Thanks a lot."

"Kristy. You are the baby-sitter. You're in charge. You'd better act like it."

Silence. Then, "You're right. Okay, Claud. I'm going to get off this phone and go and read *The Witch of Blackbird Pond*."

"Are you sure you want to read *that*?"

"I have to. It's for school. Besides, there are no such things as witches, and I'm finished with being scared. I'm a baby-sitter."

"Yes."

"Yes."

"See you in school tomorrow."

"Yes. Goodbye." Kristy hung up brusquely. She marched out of the library, got her book, and curled up with it on the living room couch. But she couldn't concentrate. She kept looking outside. The branches of the trees in Watson's yard moved eerily back and forth in front of the street lamps. They looked sort of like hands—gloved hands.

One little branch kept tap-tapping on the bay window beside Kristy's head. Tap-tap. Tap-tap.

Kristy could imagine all sorts of Hallowe'eny creatures in Watson's yard. Cackling witches, howling goblins, silent, watching ghouls.

Tap-tap. Tap-tap.

Then Kristy heard another sound. Or

218

thought she did. A sort of swooshing. It was followed by an angry yowl at the front door. "Boo-Boo!" cried Kristy. She was glad he was coming in on his own. She could stop worrying about Mrs Porter and her garden.

Kristy ran into the front hall and flung the door open.

There was Boo-Boo all right. But he wasn't alone. He was in the black-clothed arms of . . . Morbidda Destiny!

It was the first time Kristy had actually seen her, although she had imagined her vividly after Mary Anne's encounter. No wonder Karen thought she was a witch. An old, whiskery face with snappish little eyes sat under a mop of frowsty grey hair. And sure enough, she was wearing a long, black dress. Watson said Mrs Porter was just eccentric, but Kristy was not at all sure.

She gasped when she saw her.

"This cat," said Morbidda Destiny, "was in my front porch."

"I—I'm sorry," said Kristy. "He got out by accident. I hope he wasn't bothering you."

Morbidda Destiny deposited Boo-Boo in an ungraceful heap in Watson's hall. Boo-Boo tore out of the hall, heading for the laundry room.

"Wasn't *bothering* me?" cried Morbidda Destiny. "Do you know what he was *doing* in my porch, girlie?"

Kristy shook her head.

"He was eating a field mouse, that's what. And do you know what's left in my porch now?"

Kristy shook her head again, shuddering.

"A bit of fur, a bit of tail, and—"

"I'm so sorry, Mor—Mrs Porter," Kristy interrupted. "I'd like to come over and clean it up, but I'm baby-sitting here and I can't leave the—"

"Never you mind. I've taken care of it." Morbidda Destiny reached into her robes, pulled out a small paper bag, and thrust it at Kristy. "These are the remains. You get rid of them."

She turned and flapped into the night.

Now I'll prove to you just how smart Kristy is. Kristy said that just then, when Mrs Porter shoved that bag into her hands, she was really scared. And she was really disgusted by what was in the bag. But do you know what her first thought was? It was that if Mrs Porter were a true witch, she would have kept the bag for herself because she could have used the mouse fur and mouse tail in her spells. So even though Kristy was shaking all over, she was relieved too.

She looked for Boo-Boo and found him curled up in a laundry basket in front of the washing machine. He wasn't asleep—he was just resting and staring—which was a little creepy, but he seemed fine.

When Watson got home, Kristy told him

about Boo-Boo and the field mouse and the paper bag. Watson said he would speak to Mrs Porter the next morning. Then Kristy told him about Karen and the freckle-spell.

"I can't tell whether she believes in the spell or whether it's all a big game, but I thought you should know," she said.

"Thank you, Kristy. I appreciate your concern. It seems that she's been talking about witches at school, too."

"Well, I'd better call Mum," said Kristy.

She had to wait fifteen minutes for her mother to pick her up, and even though Watson was there with her, Kristy said that the whole time she kept waiting for the phone to ring again.

8th CHAPTER

Saturday, October 25th

Last night I sat for Charlotte Johanssen. She's a nice little kid, an only child, and absolutely no problem. In fact, she's timid and shy, which bothers me sometimes. It makes me feel I have to be brave and protective when I'm near her. And sometimes I don't feel brave at all. Like last night. I was already worried about the Phantom and phone calls. I mean, after the experiences Kristy and Claudia have had, who wouldn't be? So when the storm came, I nearly fell apart. Luckily, though, I'm a good baby-sitter, and when you're a good baby-sitter, baby-sitting comes first. So somehow, I managed to keep my head.

Hmphh. If that's what Stacey calls keeping her head, I wouldn't want to see her lose it.

Stacey left for the Johanssens' after an early supper. She was going to be sitting until ten, the latest she's allowed out. If you cut through Stacey's back garden and turn right, the Johanssen's house is just two doors down—a three-minute walk. If you use the streets and go round the long way, it takes about ten minutes. Stacey used the short cut, even though the night seemed darker than usual and she had to carry a torch.

Mr Johanssen met her at the front door. (His wife is hardly ever around. She's a doctor, and spends a lot of time at Stoneybrook General Hospital.) "Hi, Stacey," he greeted her. "I'm glad you could come. I'll be meeting Dr Johanssen at the cinema. The number is by the phone. We're going to see an early film and then have a bite to eat at Renwick's. That number is written down, too. I know you need to be home by ten.

"Charlotte has finished her dinner and ought to be in bed by nine-thirty, okay?"

Stacey nodded.

"I think you know everything else."

Stacey nodded again, and smiled as Charlotte came into the kitchen. "Charlotte and I will have lots of fun, won't we?"

"Yes," replied Charlotte uncertainly. "Daddy, do you have to go?"

Mr Johanssen put his arm around

Charlotte. "Mummy and I have been looking forward to this film. It's a real treat for us. But you'll have a treat when you wake up tomorrow."

"What?" asked Charlotte excitedly.

"Mummy will be here, and she's not working this weekend."

"Goody!"

Now, all the time Stacey and Charlotte and Mr Johanssen were talking, Stacey had been noticing something. If the evening had seemed dark on her way over to the Johanssens', it was positively black just ten minutes later. And it was only six-thirty. It seemed rather windy, too. The branches of the trees, already half bare, were being tossed back and forth. Stacey thought she heard thunder in the distance, but she tried not to worry about it. We'd had a lot of late-season storms, and most of them didn't last long.

Mr Johanssen left a few moments later, taking an umbrella with him. Stacey and Charlotte stood at the front window and watched his car back slowly down the drive and turn onto the street. Just as the head-lights disappeared from view, the rain started. It came pouring down, as if some-one had overturned a huge bucket of water in the sky.

"Close all the windows!" cried Charlotte.

"Turn on the lights!" cried Stacey, already frightened.

224

Stacey and Charlotte ran through the house, closing windows (there weren't many open) and turning on lights.

"What do you want to do now?" asked Stacey, when they had finished.

"Watch TV," replied Charlotte.

Crash! A huge clap of thunder sounded, and Charlotte raced to Stacey's side. "I *hate* thunder," she confessed.

"You, too?" asked Stacey. "D'you know what I used to during a thunderstorm?"

"What?"

"Hide in the linen cupboard. It was the smallest cupboard in our flat in New York City. I'd run in, slide under the bottom shelf, and close the door after me, pulling it from the bottom. Sometimes I'd take my teddy with me."

Charlotte giggled. "Once," she said, "I hid under my bed during a storm. The storm lasted so long I fell asleep and Mummy and Daddy didn't know where I was. They almost called the police!"

Crash! Ba-room! More thunder. Lightning flashed and zigzagged through the sky.

"Quick, let's put on the TV," said Stacey.

She and Charlotte ran into the family room. Charlotte flicked on the TV, and Stacey found the remote control unit. They started switching from channel to channel. They found an interview, a cooking show, and two news programmes.

"Boring," said Stacey. "Let's put on the

video. At least we could watch a good film. Where's your video?"

"We don't have a video," said Charlotte. "Not yet. Daddy said maybe this winter."

"Rats," said Stacey. She went back to the remote control.

Flick, flick, flick. They looked at all the usual channels.

"Boring, boring, boring," said Stacey.

"Double rats," said Charlotte.

"Hey," said Stacey. "Here's something." She had tuned into Channel 47. A large, ghostly hand was walking round in a cemetery all by itself. At the top of the screen were the words SPOOK THEATRE and under them, WATCH AT YOUR OWN RISK.

"Ooh, spooky!" said Charlotte. She edged closer to Stacey on the couch.

"Shall we try it?" asked Stacey. "It's better than anything else on."

"Okay," agreed Charlotte.

Stacey and Charlotte watched a commercial that showed a bottle of cleansing fluid dancing round a bathroom. Then SPOOK THEATRE appeared on the screen again, and finally the film began. It started with a night-time shot of a huge gloomy mansion sitting alone on a rise of land. Lightning flashed and thunder rumbled.

"Like our weather," Charlotte remarked, as a clap of real thunder sounded, followed by a streak of lightning. The lamps flickered.

Charlotte moved as close to Stacey as she could get without sitting in her lap. Stacey put her arm round her. They looked at each other and giggled.

"I have goose pimples!" exclaimed Charlotte.

On the television, the scene changed to a bedroom inside the mansion. It was lit only by two candles. A young woman with long, dark hair glided into the room. She was wearing a white dressing gown and carrying another candle.

She walked across the room to a set of French windows that opened onto a balcony, and began to close them, the wind from the storm making her gown billow softly around her. Just when she had almost pulled the doors shut, she gasped and let out a small cry.

"What?" whispered Charlotte.

On the lawn below the woman, Stacey and Charlotte could make out a dark figure.

"Lenora," wailed the figure, "I've come back. Back from beyond the grave."

Lenora moaned and dropped her candle. Thunder crashed. Then thunder from the real storm outside crashed even more loudly. For a moment, the room Stacey and Charlotte were in seemed to glow brightly. A second later, it was plunged into darkness.

The girls screamed. Charlotte clutched

Stacey. Everything had gone off—the lights, the TV, all the electricity. It was so quiet they could hear their own hearts pounding. But worse than the silence was the utter blackness.

"Power cut," whispered Stacey.

"I want my mummy," murmured Charlotte. "Or my daddy."

Stacey tried to pull herself together. "There's really nothing to be afraid of," she told Charlotte. "So the electricity went off. So what? The pilgrims lived their whole lives without electricity. You should be in New York when there's a power cut. The entire city practically stops running. We lived on the seventeenth floor of a block of flats and when the power went off, so did the lifts. Imagine having to walk up seventeen flights of stairs just to get home."

"Yuck," said Charlotte.

"I'll say. Now," Stacey went on, feeling a bit better, "what we have to do is get some candles."

"Like Lenora's?" asked Charlotte.

"Well, yes. Where do your parents keep them?"

"I don't know. I'm not allowed to light matches."

"Don't you have any idea?"

"Maybe in the chest of drawers in the dining room."

"Good. All right, now we'll just find my torch and we can use it to light our way into

228

the dining room."

Stacey stood up, holding tightly to Charlotte's hand. They began edging toward the front hall where Stacey had left her jacket and the torch.

Shuffle, shuffle, shuffle, *crash!*

"Ow! yelled Stacey.

"What?"

"My toe. I walked into something." Stacey felt around. "A table, I think. Okay, let's keep going."

Shuffle, shuffle, shuffle.

"Stacey?"

"What, Charlotte?"

Shuffle, shuffle, shuffle.

"I hear something."

"What?"

"I don't know."

Shuffle, shuffle, shuffle.

"There it is again. Stop moving."

Stacey and Charlotte paused, holding their breaths and listening.

And then Stacey heard it—a creak.

"Where's it coming from?" she asked.

"Sounds like the basement," whispered Charlotte.

"Well, let's make sure the door to the basement is closed. Where *is* the door to the basement?"

"Just here." Charlotte moved past Stacey, running her hand along the wall. "Yup, it's closed."

"Okay. Good. Be quiet for a sec."

The girls stopped and listened again.

Creak. Creak, squish, creak, squish, creak, squish.

In the dark, Charlotte's hand found Stacey's. She held on tight.

Creak, squish, creak, squish.

"Something's coming up the stairs!" cried Charlotte softly.

"Shh," was all Stacey said, but she told me later that what she was thinking was, Oh gosh! It's the Phantom. He's turned off the electricity to distract us, and now he's sneaking into the Johanssens' house through the basement!

Creak, squish. The sound was closer. It had almost reached the top of the stairs.

Stacey was just about to tell Charlotte to start heading for the back door, when the creaking stopped. It was followed by a *woof!*

Stacey jumped about a foot, but Charlotte exclaimed, "Carrot! Oh, it's just Carrot! He must have come in through the basement again. There's a broken window down there."

"Who's Carrot?"

"Our schnauzer. He must be sopping. I'll try to find a towel so we can dry him off."

And at that moment the lights came back on. Stacey and Charlotte looked at each other and began to giggle. Then they did dry off the poor, rain-drenched Carrot, and they even watched some more of *Spook Theatre*.

Outside the storm died down, and the rest of the evening was peaceful.

The phone didn't ring once while Stacey was at the Johanssens'.

9th
CHAPTER

Saturday, October 25

This evening I baby-sat for David Michael. The rest of the Thomases went out for dinner with Watson and Karen and Andrew, but David Michael had to stay at home in bed because he's got a cold.

I like baby-sitting for David Michael. He's almost like my brother. I've known him since he was born. And he's usually pretty good. But tonight, since he's sick, he fell asleep very early, and I felt all alone. I couldn't think of anything except prowlers and weird phone calls and especially the Phantom. The weather was fine — a little breezy, but not stormy — and there were

Spooked isn't the word. Mary Anne was practically out of her mind. She was sitting quietly on the couch watching an old *I Love Lucy* show, when suddenly she got goose pimples all along her arms. She jumped up, turned down the volume on the TV, and listened. Nothing. Not a thing. Even so, she dashed upstairs to check on David Michael. He was lying on his side, breathing noisily, a box of Kleenex next to him. Mary Anne left the landing light on and went back downstairs.

She closed every open cupboard door and turned on two more lights. Then she closed the laundry room door, in case someone was hiding there. Finally, she pulled down the venetian blinds in the kitchen. But still she didn't feel safe, even though Louie, the Thomases' dog, was in the house with her.

What if someone sneaks inside while I'm watching TV? she thought. That was when she decided to rig up the burglar alarms. All three of them.

Now, the thing about Mary Anne Spier is that she may be quiet, and she may be shy, but she *does* have a good sense of humour and a good imagination. You'd have to, to think up the alarms that Mary Anne rigged in the Thomases' house.

Well, actually, the first one wasn't much

in terms of imagination. It was the alarm Mary Anne had described at our emergency club meeting the week before: a big stack of pots, pans, and tins from the kitchen built up against the inside of the door into the garage. If anyone tried to get in from the garage, the door would push the stack over and it would crash down, alerting Mary Anne, who would be able to escape out of another door and call the police. The burglar might even be so startled that he'd turn round and leave.

Mary Anne finished her alarm, sat down in front of the TV again, and immediately decided she ought to rig up the front door, too. She was pretty sure a prowler wouldn't come through the front door, but you can never tell with prowlers. She had used up all the pots, pans, and tins, though, so she had to think of something else. She looked at a shelf full of David Michael's toys and her eyes fell on a large bag of marbles.

"*Aha*!" she said aloud.

Mary Anne took the marbles into the front hall. Then she found a long piece of string. She placed the bag of marbles on a table next to the door and attached the string to a little hole near the opening of the bag. She tied the other end securely to the doorknob. This was Mary Anne's idea: the prowler quietly opens the door, the string pulls the marbles to the floor; they spill everywhere, not only making a racket to alert Mary Anne, but causing the prowler to slip and fall when he steps inside.

Naturally, as soon as Mary Anne finished her second alarm, she decided she needed one for the back door. It was the only way she would feel safe. Then she would have all the doors covered.

Mary Anne had to think for a while before making that last alarm. By then, she had no more marbles as well as no more pots and pans.

What else could make a lot of noise? Mary Anne thought.

Blocks? Maybe.

Toys? No.

Music! Music could be good and loud. The plans for Mary Anne's final alarm began to take shape.

First she tiptoed upstairs to Kristy's room to borrow her portable cassette player. Then she looked through the tape collection in the room Sam and Charlie share. She selected one called "Poundin' Down the Walls" by the Slime Kings and slipped it into the machine.

Back downstairs she sat on the rug in the den to think, cassette player in her lap. How could she arrange for it to turn itself on?

She thought some more. How did *she* turn it on? She pressed the play button, of course. Okay. How could she get something else to press the play button? Better still, how could she get the back door to press the play button?

In a flash of brilliance, she had the answer. Mary Anne leaped up and carried the cassette player into the kitchen. She sat down on the floor again and examined the skinny, rubber-tipped doorstop attached to the bottom of the back door. Perfect.

Mary Anne set the player about two feet from the door. She lined the doorstop up with the play button. Then she opened the door. The doorstop hit the player and the player fell over. But that didn't stop Mary Anne. I need to . . . to shore it up or something, she thought.

She dragged a heavy, round stool in from the kitchen and set it just behind the player.

She opened the door again.

The doorstop hit the play button, and "Poundin' Down the Walls" blared out of the machine. Mary Anne smiled. Satisfied, she pressed the stop button, turned the volume up to ten, and went back into the lounge. She curled up on the couch with her tattered copy of *The Secret Garden* and began to read.

She was in the middle of one of her favourite parts—the part where Mary discovers poor, sickly Colin hidden in Misselthwaite Manor—when she heard an ominous creak from the front hall. Actually, Mary Anne told me the next day, it was just a little creak, but her head was filled with the dark, shadowy hallways of Misselthwaite,

236

so almost any noise would have sounded ominous.

Mary Anne looked up sharply. She jumped to her feet. "Louie!" she whispered urgently. Where is that dog when you need protection? she asked herself. She tiptoed to the lounge door and peeped into the hall.

There was Louie. He was standing at attention, staring at the front door.

The hinges creaked slightly.

Louie whined.

And all of a sudden the door flew open, pulling the marbles to the floor and scattering them loudly.

Louie barked twice.

But no one came in.

Mary Anne let out a sigh of relief. "It's just the wind, Louie," she said shakily, "like the wind off the moors in Yorkshire," she added, thinking of her book. "I must not have closed the door properly."

But Louie didn't look convinced. He sat at the door, silently begging to be let out to patrol the property. Mary Anne opened it for him, and then set to work gathering up the marbles. She put them back in the bag, but decided not to rig the alarm again. She settled for double-locking the door.

Then she returned to *The Secret Garden*. In the story, Mary was having her first conversation with Colin. Suddenly Mary Anne heard a soft thud.

And then—to her absolute horror—

"Poundin' Down the Walls" blasted on in the kitchen!

Mary Anne let out a bloodcurdling scream as she gazed at the partly open back door. She was just about to make a dash for the front door, when Louie strolled into the kitchen, sniffed curiously at the cassette player, and headed for his water bowl.

"Louie!" exclaimed Mary Anne in a half gasp, half shriek.

She'd forgotten that David Michael had taught Louie how to throw his weight against doors. If they weren't latched properly, they opened, which was occasionally useful to Louie. Mary Anne probably hadn't closed the back door tightly after she'd tested the alarm.

"Some baby-sitter I am," she scolded herself, "leaving doors open right and left for anybody to walk through."

"Bary Add!" called a voice.

Mary Anne looked around to see David Michael standing sleepily on the stairs, his old stuffed dog in one hand.

"Bary Add, cad you put the busic off!" he asked. "I do't like it. It's too loud." He blinked in the bright light of the hall.

"Oh, gosh! I'm sorry, David Michael," cried Mary Anne. "I didn't mean to wake you up. Really."

She dashed to the player and turned it off. "That was an accident. I'm sorry . . . How are you feeling?"

"Stuffy. Ad by head hurts."

"Oh," said Mary Anne sympathetically. She remembered that Mrs Thomas had said David Michael could have half a paracetamol if he needed it. "Do you want some paracetamol?" she asked him. "It'll make your head feel better."

"Okay," said David Michael wheezily.

"You go back to bed and I'll be up in a minute."

Mary Anne felt better since the house wasn't so quiet. She brought David Michael the paracetamol, and then she sat on his bed and told him a story about a tiny man named Mr Pieball who lived in the woods on the twelfth floor of a block of flats in an old tree with his miniature collie, Louie.

David Michael fell asleep with a smile on his lips.

Mary Anne was just closing the door to his room when she heard a tremendous crash downstairs.

The tin-can burglar alarm! It had gone off and Mary Anne was trapped upstairs where there was no escape route! Heart pounding, she tried to work out what to do. Should she wake David Michael and bring him into Mrs Thomas's room while she called the police? Should she risk everything and make a dash for the front door? What if it was just Louie fooling around? Maybe she should call Stacey and try out our code. If only she could remember it . . .

"Mary Anne?" said an uncertain voice from downstairs.

Yikes! It was a *man's* voice!

Mary Anne shrank into a corner of the landing.

"Mary Anne?" it called again more loudly.

The voice sounded vaguely familiar. How does the Phantom know my name? wondered Mary Anne.

Then she heard another voice call her. It was Kristy.

Mary Anne dared to peep downstairs. Kristy, Sam, Charlie, Mrs Thomas, Watson, Karen, and Andrew were standing in a group at the bottom of the stairs looking up at her.

"Oh," said Mary Anne, trying to sound nonchalant, and realizing the first voice had been Watson's. "I thought I heard you. I just gave David Michael some paracetamol and got him back to sleep. He woke up with a headache." She trotted down the stairs.

"Um . . . Mary Anne . . . if you don't mind my asking," said Mrs Thomas, "what are all those tins and things doing by the door?"

"Oh *those*?" replied Mary Anne. "Those are just . . . just . . . Actually, they were a sort of burglar alarm. I meant to put them away before you got home."

Kristy began to giggle. Charlie snorted.

"And my cassette player?" asked Kristy.

Mary Anne demonstrated the back-door

alarm, this time with the volume turned down.

"Ingenious," commented Watson.

"It certainly looks as if David Michael is safe with you," said Mrs Thomas.

Mary Anne nodded. She knew she was blushing furiously.

"You could start another business of your own," said Sam. "Mary Anne's Surefire Alarm Systems."

Mary Anne blushed even more furiously.

"Come on," said Kristy, after Mrs Thomas had paid Mary Anne. "I'll walk you home." And she did.

10th CHAPTER

Boy trouble.

So far, the Babysitters Club had managed to keep boys and boy trouble pretty much out of the meetings.

But not on Monday, October the twenty-seventh. At that meeting, we were trying to discuss baby-sitting problems, but the subject of boys kept coming up instead. Kristy started it.

"Do you know what Alan Gray did to me today?" she asked, a look of pure disgust on her face.

"What made you think of Alan Gray?" I asked. We'd been talking about Charlotte Johanssen.

"Everything makes me think about him," said Kristy, throwing her hands in the air. "He bothers me all the time, every single second of every single day."

"He's not bothering you right now," said

242

Mary Anne.

"Yes, he is. He bothers me just by living. Alan Gray is so horrible whenever he's near me, that he's all I can think about."

"So what did he do to you today?" asked Stacey.

"He hid my maths homework, and then when it was time to hand it in and I couldn't find it, he jumped up and said to Mr Peters, "Excuse me, but I know where Kristy's paper is. Her little brother ate it. Kristy wouldn't give him breakfast and he was starving."

I giggled.

Kristy turned on me, eyes flashing.

"Well, I'm sorry, I think it's rather funny."

"You would."

"Oh, Kristy," I said with a laugh. "Calm down."

"But it's not just that," she went on. (I could see that Kristy was determined to be upset.) "I think he's getting worse. On Friday he hid my shoes. On Thursday he called me a skinny pipsqueak in front of the class, and twice last week I caught him looking in my desk in the morning. Every day it's something. He never stops."

"Why don't you talk to . . . to Sam about it?" suggested Stacey.

"My own *brother*? No way. Besides, he'd never understand. He's girl-crazy. You should have seen who—or maybe I should say *what*—he took to the pictures last Friday. She's new at school and she had spiky yellow hair with green stuff at the ends, and these little lace gloves with the fingertips cut out. Now, what is the point of wearing gloves if—"

Kristy stopped talking when she realized that the rest of us were staring at her.

"What? What is it?" she finally asked. Then she noticed Stacey, who was sitting on my bed, gazing sadly down at her hands.

"Sam took a high school girl to the pictures?" she asked softly.

"Yeah, I—Oh, no, Stacey, I'm sorry." Kristy had forgotten all about Stacey's crush on Sam. "I'm sure it doesn't mean anything. He *is* interested in you. Really."

"Then what about that girl—"

"Tamara? You mean, why did he take her to the pictures? Honestly, I don't know. But she was so weird. Sam'll never be serious about her. I'm positive. I think he went out with her just to shake Mum up."

"I thought he liked me," said Stacey.

"He does, he does," Kristy assured her.

"What do you mean when you say she's weird?" asked Stacey carefully.

"Well, the green-tipped hair, for one thing. And the clothes. Her clothes were just . . . just *weird*."

"Like mine?" I asked suspiciously.

"Oh, no, not at all like yours," said

Kristy, beginning to blush. "*Nothing* like yours."

I glanced at Stacey. For the first time since I'd met her, she didn't seem so sophisticated. In fact, she looked like a lost little girl. Two tears slid slowly down her cheeks.

"Oh, no! Please don't cry!" exclaimed Kristy.

Mary Anne jumped up from her spot on the floor and sat down next to Stacey. She can't stand people to be upset.

The phone rang and I answered it. It was Mr Willis from down the street. I'd baby-sat for his kids once before.

"Yes?" I said. "This Saturday? Yes, of course . . . Eight p.m. . . . Sure, I'll be there." I hung up the phone and noted my job in my record book.

When I looked up, everyone was glaring at me, even Stacey. It was my turn to find out what I'd had done wrong.

"Okay, what is it?" I asked.

"Did you just accept that job?" Kristy demanded.

I felt my stomach drop. "Yes," I whispered.

"But Claudia, you know the rule."

Of course I knew. I'd just forgotten. "I'm supposed to check with everyone else first."

Kristy nodded. "I'm free on Saturday."

"So am I," said Mary Anne.

"Oh," I said.

"I'm not," said Stacey, "but I wish you'd asked me. You didn't know I was busy."

"I—I'll call him back," I suggested. "One of you can have the job."

"No," said Kristy. "That makes us look disorganized. You keep the job. But I want to know something. How often do you get calls for the club and accept jobs without asking anyone else first?"

"Oh, not often. I mean, almost never. Only . . . only once before."

"That job with the Newtons?"

"All right, twice, then."

"You mean that job with Charlotte?" asked Stacey.

"Oh, all right, three times."

"Claudia!" exclaimed Kristy.

"I don't do it on purpose!" I exploded. "I'm not trying to cheat you, you know."

"We d—"

"It's just that I have so much on my mind."

"What's wrong?" asked Mary Anne.

"The Hallowe'en Hop is only four days away and I don't think Trevor even knows my name yet."

"Wow," said Stacey sympathetically. "I didn't realize it was getting that serious."

I nodded. "I guess there's no hope now."

"Yes, there is!" Mary Anne cried suddenly. "Where there's time, there's hope! And you've got four days. Anything could happen in four days."

"I think you should talk to him," said Kristy.

"I think you should ask him to the dance," said Stacey.

I gasped. "No way! This isn't a girls' invitation dance. I can't ask a boy to go with me."

"In New York we did it all the time."

"Well, this isn't New York. It's little Stoneybrook. And I am not asking Trevor Sandbourne to the Hallowe'en Hop."

"You're scared," said Stacey.

"You're right."

"Maybe Trevor is scared, too."

"You think so? He is sensitive . . ."

Before Stacey could answer, the phone rang again.

"*I'll* get it," said Kristy meaningfully, reaching for the receiver. "Hello? . . . Hi, Mr Newton. Where are you? At the office? . . . Oh. . . . *Oh* . . ."

"What?" I asked.

Kristy waved at me to be quiet. "Now?" we heard her say. "But I thought the baby wasn't due for three more weeks . . . Oh . . . Mmhmm. . . . Jamie called you? . . . I didn't know he could use the phone, either. . . . Yes. . . . Right. . . . Okay, we'll be here. 'Bye."

"The baby?" squealed Mary Anne. "Already?"

"I guess so," replied Kristy. "Mr Newton said that Jamie had just called him at the office and said he wanted him to come home. When Mr Newton asked if the baby was on the way, Jamie said yes!"

"Oooh! I can't believe it!" I cried.

"So Mr Newton says he'll probably need one of us to stay with Jamie this evening. If he's going to be at the hospital really late, Jamie can just spend the night at our house, I expect. He's done that once before. Mr Newton will call as soon as he gets home."

"Gosh, I hope Mrs Newton's all right," said Stacey. "I mean, asking Jamie to call Mr Newton, and the baby coming early and everything."

"Yeah, you're right," I said.

For a moment we forgot our boy problems.

"Are babies who are born three weeks early usually okay?" I asked.

The other members of the Babysitters Club shrugged. "Don't know," said Mary Anne.

"I once heard of a baby who was born three *months* early," said Stacey. "He had to stay in hospital practically for ever, but now he's okay."

"David Michael was two weeks early," put in Kristy, "and he was just a little small. The doctors made him stay in hospital three extra days to gain more weight, but he was fine.

"You know something?" said Mary Anne. "I don't even know whether I was born early or late or on time. Dad hardly ever talks about things like that—you know, what I did when I was a baby. It's times like this when I wish I had a mother. I bet she'd talk about those things."

For a moment nobody said anything. I saw Stacey looking sympathetically at Mary Anne. Stacey once told me she wished she knew her better, but Mary Anne is still a little shy when she's near Stacey.

Then Kristy broke the silence (as usual) and saved the day. "You know what?" she said to Mary Anne. "You should ask my mother those things. Or ask Mrs Kishi or Mimi. I bet they'd know, since we all grew up together. My mum told me once that when we were really little, about a year old, our parents formed a playgroup for us, so we could be with kids our own age, and they could talk about child rearing and so on. They must have known all three of us pretty well."

"Really?" asked Mary Anne. "Maybe I will ask one of them . . . some day."

The phone jangled. "Mr Newton!" cried Kristy, as she dived for the receiver. "Baby-sitters Club," she said officially, and I realized I'd forgotten to do that earlier. Another point against me. Kristy nodded at us to let us know that it was Mr Newton on the phone. We watched her face anxiously. "It was?" she said, looking disappointed. "Oh . . . oh . . . Sure, we understand.

Actually, I'm glad the baby's not coming early. It'll be better for him—or her—to be on time. . . . Right. . . . Right. No problem. Okay, see you soon. 'Bye." Kristy hung up the phone.

"False alarm?" I asked.

"You could say that." Kristy began to giggle.

"What's so funny?"

"Mrs Newton is fine. She didn't even know Jamie was using the phone. You know how Jamie always wants to talk to his dad and waits for him to come home from work every day?"

We nodded.

"Well, today he got tired of waiting and just went ahead and called his father for a chat. Mrs Newton had taught him how to dial the number in case there ever *was* an emergency with the baby or something, only Mr Newton didn't know that. Anyway, Jamie told Mr Newton he wanted him to come home—because he always wants him to come home — and Mr Newton asked if the baby was on the way, and Jamie said yes—because of course a baby *is* on the way in his house and—oh, it was just a big mix-up!"

We all began to laugh.

"It'll be pretty exciting when the baby really does come," said Mary Anne.

"It would be pretty exciting if Trevor

asked me to the dance," I added. I sighed loudly.

If I had known what was going to happen that very night, I might not have bothered sighing over Trevor. He was nothing compared to the other problems that were about to come up.

11th
CHAPTER

After dinner that night, it was Mimi's turn to help me with my homework.

"Mostly maths," I told her ruefully as we settled ourselves at the kitchen table. "We're having a test on Thursday and Mr Peters gave us revision problems. And he gave me extra work. Only me, Mimi. No one else," I grumbled.

"And what is this work, my Claudia?"

"Memorizing the times tables. Mr Peters knows that someone helps me with my homework, and he said I must drill them tonight. You're supposed to go through the pack of flashcards twice with me. Boring, boring. I haven't done that since juniors."

"It is just revision, my Claudia. The memorization helps. When you know the tables just like that"—Mimi snapped her fingers—"your maths will go much faster."

"Well, I like anything that makes it go faster."

Mimi smiled. "All right. We will go right through the pack. The cards are not in order." She held one up. "Six times seven."

"Forty. I mean, forty-two."

"Eight times three."

"Twenty-four."

"Good girl."

We were about halfway through the box when the doorbell rang. Mimi knew I needed a break. "Why don't you answer the door, my Claudia?"

I leaped to my feet. When I reached the door, I peeped out the front window to see who was there, and was surprised to see Mr and Mrs Goldman from next door. They're an older couple who don't have any children and travel a lot, so we don't see much of them. As far as I could remember, they'd never come over without calling first.

"Mum!" I yelled as I unlatched the chain. "Dad! It's the Goldmans."

"Hi," I said, opening the door.

"Claudia, dear," said Mrs Goldman. She was clutching her husband's arm and looked terrified.

"We're sorry to disturb you," Mr Goldman said.

My parents appeared behind me. "Eileen, Arnold," said my mother. "Please come in. Is anything wrong?"

The Goldmans stepped into the foyer.

"We think we've been robbed," said Mr Goldman shakily. "We went out to dinner and when we came back just now, the front door was open a crack—"

"—and I'm positive I left the light on in the living room," said Mrs Goldman tearfully, "but the house is dark."

My heart began to pump faster. It sounded as if it were beating right in my ears.

"We were afraid to go inside," said Mr Goldman. He was twisting his hat practically into knots.

"We're glad you came over," said my mother. "I think it was wise not to go in the house. You just never know." She patted Mrs Goldman's arm.

"I'll call the police," said Dad.

"And I'll make some tea," added Mimi, who had joined us.

Two policemen showed up quickly, before Mimi even had a chance to pour the tea. They listened to the Goldmans' story, then went next door to check the house. When they returned, one said, "Well, I'm afraid you *have* been robbed. The place is a bit messy upstairs. However, the intruder, or intruders, has gone now. I think you can return safely."

Mr Goldman nodded.

"Tell me, sir," said the younger policeman, "did anything unusual happen today? An odd phone call, anything like that?"

Mr Goldman shook his head. "No, I'd—"

But his wife interrupted him. "Wait. There *was* a funny call, Arnold. Two, actually. They came when you were working in the cellar." She turned to the policemen. "He has a workshop down there," she explained. "Late in the afternoon the phone rang. When I answered it, I said hello twice, and then the caller just hung up. It happened again about a half an hour later."

I knew my eyes were opening wider and wider. "The Phantom Caller," I croaked.

The young policeman looked at me sharply. Then he nodded ever so slightly at his partner.

Well, as you can imagine, I had to get on the phone immediately and begin telling people about the Phantom. The first person I called was Stacey. I could almost hear her jaw drop.

"What did he get?" she squeaked.

"A pearl necklace and a gold brooch. Both very valuable. The brooch was an antique."

"I just don't understand," said Stacey. "How does he know?"

"Beats me. The police did say one interesting thing, though."

"What?"

"They said they're not sure this robbery

255

fits the Phantom's pattern. They said it might be a copycat crime. You know, just some local crook who wanted to get a little fast cash and is covering his tracks by disguising the crime as the Phantom's. The police said they were very surprised to see the Phantom working a neighbourhood like ours."

"What's that supposed to mean?"

"It means usually he sticks to millionaires."

"Oh."

After I talked to Stacey, I got on the phone to Kristy and told her the news. She said she would call Mary Anne. Then Mimi made me return to my homework. We were almost finished with the flashcards when the phone rang. Mimi answered it, then handed it to me. "It is Kristy," she told me. "Please speak for only a few minutes."

"Okay. Thanks," I said, smiling at Mimi as she handed me the receiver. Mimi is the only one who lets me take phone calls during the homework sessions.

"Claudia," said Kristy, not even answering my hello, "we have a big problem."

"What?" I asked with a groan.

"I should never have told Mary Anne about the Goldmans, although she would have found out anyway."

"What happened?"

"She told her father about the robbery and he's forbidden her to do any baby-sitting until the Phantom is caught."

"Oh, no."

"And she's got three jobs lined up this week."

"Oh, *no*."

"Yeah. I think her father is actually just mad that she was on the phone after dinner and not discussing homework. You know his silly rule."

"I know."

"But we still have to cover for her. I'm calling an emergency club meeting during break tomorrow."

"Okay. I'll see you in school." We hung up.

When we finally finished my homework, Mimi came upstairs and sat for her portrait again. I was working on her eyes, which were the hardest part for me. When Mimi looks at me, I see all sorts of things expressed in her eyes. I wanted very badly to show that on the canvas, and it was difficult.

"How are you and Janine getting on?" asked Mimi, remembering the conversation we'd had the last time she'd posed for me.

"The same," I said.

"You know, my Claudia, that in order for things to change, *you* must change them. You will grow to be an old woman like me, if you wait for others to change things that do not please you."

I thought about that. I thought about the times Janine had tried to talk to me and I had brushed her off. I thought about the times I had been cross with her, without telling her why I was cross. But all I said to Mimi was, "When I'm an old woman, I hope I'm just like you."

Mimi smiled.

I added flecks of light to the pupils in Mimi's portrait and her eyes looked almost right.

The next day, school was buzzing about the Goldmans' robbery. Word had spread quickly. Was it the Phantom or not? Had he really come to Stoneybrook? Should our parents buy fancy alarm systems for our houses? Should we put our valuables in safe-deposit boxes at the bank? The one thing everyone agreed on was that if the robber really was the Phantom, we didn't have anything to worry about *personally*. He usually only struck when a home was empty, and he had never injured anyone. No one had even seen him.

I spent maths class that day trying to design a plan of attack on Trevor Sandbourne. It was Tuesday. The Hallowe'en Hop was on Friday, just three days away. I knew that I could not, as Stacey had suggested, ask *him* to the dance, but I could try to attract his attention, get him to notice me.

At lunchtime, I bought the hot lunch—meat loaf, green beans, and mashed potatoes (all prime candidates for a food sculpture). Dessert was—what else?—red jelly. As I was walking toward the table where Stacey, Dorianne, Emily, and the boys were sitting, I noticed Trevor just a couple of tables away from them.

Aha, I thought, I can start doing something to get Trevor to notice me. I decided to take a shortcut to my table, which would involve squeezing by Trevor. Maybe I could say hi to him while I was at it.

I approached him, holding my tray tightly. Trevor was sitting at the end of his table. I squeezed round behind him, and just as I did so, the kid seated behind Trevor stood up suddenly. I lost my balance — and my plate of jelly slid off my tray and landed jelly-side-down in Trevor's lap. Very slowly, he looked at it, then at me, while red stuff oozed to the floor.

His face turned as red as the jelly.

I knew mine was red, too.

What I didn't know was what I was supposed to do. Everyone at Trevor's table was staring at me. A bunch of other kids were staring too. At long last I balanced my tray on one knee, handed Trevor my napkin, and said, "Sorry. I'm sorry." Then I fled to an empty seat next to Stacey. I crumpled into the chair and buried my face in my hands. "I am *so* embarrassed," I whispered. "Is everyone still looking at me?"

Stacey glanced around. "No. They're watching Trevor clean up his pants. By the way, you left the jelly plate in his lap."

"Oh, no. Oh, no."

"Hey, good doing, Claudia!" Rick exclaimed.

"Yeah, that was really coordinated," added Howie.

"Shut up, you guys," I said. My face was still flaming.

"Oooh, touch*ee*," said Pete.

Honestly, boys can be such pains. Well, some boys can be. Rick, Howie, and Pete would probably bring this incident up periodically until we graduated from high school. Maybe for the rest of our lives.

I decided that I would try to paint a picture about embarrassment. The main colour would be red.

I was glad that we needed to have an emergency meeting of the Babysitters Club because it helped me to forget that I had just blown the Hallowe'en Hop and would be sitting at home like Kristy and Mary Anne on Friday night. *They* didn't care about not going to the dance, but I sure did. (Stacey, I happened to know, was going to be invited to the dance by Pete. Pete had told Rick, who'd told Howie, who'd told Dorianne, who'd told me. And Dorianne and Emily were both going to go.)

Kristy gathered the club members beneath an unused basketball hoop in the playground. Before she could even open her mouth, Mary Anne spoke. "I just want to tell you all that I'm really sorry. This is all my fault. I'm causing problems and I feel terrible."

"It's not you, it's your father," said Kristy.

"I know, but you three have to take over all my work."

"Don't worry about it," said Stacey.

"That's right," I added. "Every business faces problems sometimes. Mimi says that solving problems strengthens character."

Mary Anne smiled. "Mimi is usually right."

"Okay," said Kristy, rubbing her hands together. "Let's get to work." She opened our appointment book, which she'd been carrying under one arm. "Hmm. Mary Anne, you're supposed to be sitting for the Marshalls for an hour this afternoon, for Claire and Margo Pike tomorrow, and for Charlotte Johanssen on Saturday morning, right?"

"Right."

"Well, let's see. Today is usually my day to watch David Michael, but I switched with Sam since Claudia and I are sitting at the Newtons' starting at five this afternoon. If Mrs Marshall really just needs someone from three-thirty to four-thirty, I could do that."

"Okay," said Mary Anne. "Here, let me

take the book and keep track of all this stuff. It's my job, anyway."

Kristy handed the book over.

"Now," said Mary Anne. "Let's take care of the Pikes. Claudia, you're not down for any jobs tomorrow."

"No, but I have my art class."

"Oh, right."

"I could skip it," I said reluctantly.

"No, I'll take your job, Mary Anne," said Stacey.

"But you're down for Charlotte."

"Oh, not any more. Dr Johanssen called last night to cancel. I didn't have a chance to change the book."

"Great. Okay, the Pikes are taken care of. That leaves Charlotte on Saturday. How come Dr Johanssen cancelled tomorrow? Maybe she'll cancel Saturday, too."

"I don't think so," said Stacey. "It was just that some meeting was called off tomorrow. It's not going to affect Saturday."

Mary Anne sighed. She looked at the book again. "Claudia?" she asked.

"Sure, I'll watch Charlotte."

Mary Anne snapped the book shut. "I've been thinking," she said firmly. "I shouldn't be part of the Babysitters Club any more.

"*What*?" Kristy and Stacey and I cried.

"It's not fair," Mary Anne went on. "Who knows how long it'll be before the Phantom is caught. Dad could keep me on baby-sitting probation for years."

"But—but—" said Kristy.

"Hey, I've got an idea!" I cried. "Why don't you stay on as secretary of the club. You keep all our records and appointments so neatly. Nobody else will do as good a job."

"Well . . ." said Mary Anne. "But I'm not going to be earning any money. I might not be able to pay my club subs."

"Let's not worry about that now," said Kristy.

"Right," I added. "Us baby-sitters have to stick together. Through thick and thin."

"Through Phantoms and power failures," said Stacey.

"Through fires and floods," said Kristy.

We put our arms round each other and headed into the school building just as the bell rang.

12th CHAPTER

Late that afternoon, Kristy and I began one of our most terrifying baby-sitting experiences ever. Jamie Newton's mother had called two weeks earlier needing a sitter for that evening. There was one hitch: Jamie would not be the only child at the Newtons'. His wild cousins would be there, too. I'd baby-sat for them once before—by myself—and based on that experience, I told Mrs Newton she would need two sitters the second time, especially since the job was at dinner time and the kids would need to be fed.

Jamie's cousins were Rob, Brenda, and Rosie. Rob, the oldest, was eight; Brenda was five; and Rosie was three. And they were tough to handle. Rob hated girls (including girl baby-sitters), Brenda was fussy, and Rosie was noisy. Well, they were *all* noisy. The other time I had sat for them, they jumped and ran round the living room and disobeyed practically everything I said. I had finally managed to calm them down, but I still wasn't looking forward to the evening, although it was bound to be different with Kristy there.

We arrived at the Newtons' at five o'clock and found the place already in chaos. The adults, Jamie's parents and Mr and Mrs Feldman (the parents of Rob, Brenda, and Rosie) were trying to get ready to leave, but three of the four kids (all but Rob) were crying, Mrs Feldman couldn't find the sandwiches she'd brought for our supper, and Mrs Newton suddenly discovered that her good coat wouldn't button round her middle any more.

"Damn," she said. "I wore this coat the entire time I was pregnant with Jamie. I just don't understand it."

"Sis?" called Mrs Feldman from the kitchen. "The sandwiches absolutely are not in the refrigerator. If they are, they're invisible. . . . Rosie, stop it. I don't know why Brenda hit you."

"Not that refrigerator. I put them in the one in the basement," Mrs Newton called back. "Get Jamie to show you. . . . What am I going to wear tonight? I can't wear that awful maternity coat, not to *this* cocktail party. . . . Roger?" she shouted upstairs to Mr Newton.

"Mummy." Jamie came sniffing into the

hall and pulled on his mother's hand. I don't want to go in the basement with Aunt Diane."

"Never mind, Sis. I found them . . . Brenda, *stop* it. You're pestering your sister."

Well, things went on that way for about five more minutes, but finally Mrs Newton found a shawl to wear instead of the coat, and, miraculously, Jamie, Brenda, and Rosie stopped crying.

The adults left.

Kristy and I looked at each other, then at the living room where the four kids were standing.

They eyed us and we eyed them.

Rob gathered his sisters in a huddle while Jamie looked on.

Suddenly the huddle broke and the Feldmans began tearing and screaming and jumping round, just as they had done when I sat for them before. That time I had ignored them, and after a while they'd quietened down.

But Kristy had a different idea. You have to remember that even though she's small for her age, she's a tomboy, and she's used to boys and a big family.

The Feldmans hadn't been screeching and tearing through the living room for more than three seconds, when Kristy put her fingers in her mouth and blew—hard. An ear-piercing whistle screamed from her lips.

The Feldmans stopped cold.

"Now hear this!" shouted Kristy. "No yelling, no running, and no jumping inside this house—and I mean it." She saw that Rob was about to say something, so she added, "One false move and I'll punch your lights out. That goes for all of you. Do you hear me?"

The Feldmans nodded.

Jamie was wide-eyed with disbelief at what his beloved Kristy had just said.

"Do you understand me?" she went on.

The Feldmans nodded.

"Any questions?"

Rob started to open his mouth again, then thought better of it and raised his hand instead.

"Yes?" said Kristy.

"How did you do that?"

"Do what?"

"Whistle with your fingers."

"Oh. Here, I'll show you. But if you learn how to do it, remember that this is usually an outdoor whistle, not an indoor one. Got it?"

"Yes."

Kristy took Rob into the basement for whistle practice and I led the three younger children into the playroom. I had just settled them into one of Jamie's favourite activities—colouring pictures of monsters—when the phone rang.

"I'll get it," I called down to Kristy. I

dashed into the kitchen. "Hello, Newtons' residence."

Nothing. I couldn't hear a sound.

"H-hello?" I tried again.

It's funny how sometimes you can be just as scared by *nothing* as by *something*. My hands were shaking as I hung up the receiver.

"Who was it?" called Kristy.

"Wrong number," I replied uneasily. I didn't want to frighten any of the children, but considering what had happened to the Goldmans the night before, I suddenly thought I had good reason to be nervous.

As soon as possible, I would tell Kristy about the call in private.

A half an hour later, just as I was beginning to think about supper, the phone rang again.

Kristy was coming up the stairs with Rob, who looked very proud of himself. "I'll get the phone this time," she said.

I nodded and followed her into the kitchen.

"Hello?" she said. "Hello?"

I could tell immediately that it was another one of *those* calls.

Kristy hung up the phone, looking nervous. I glanced into the playroom to make sure all the kids were busy. "No one there?" I asked Kristy.

She shook her head.

"The first call was like that, too. It wasn't

really a wrong number."

Kristy bit her lip. "What do you think?" she whispered. "Is it time for the Phantom to strike again?"

I shrugged. "Do you think it could be Sam goof-calling?" Kristy's brother had quite a reputation. And he liked to give the Babysitters Club a hard time every now and then.

"It's possible," said Kristy thoughtfully. "He's pretty interested in this Phantom business, but it's not like Sam to call and not say anything. He kind of likes to leave his mark, if you know what I mean. It'd be more like him to get on the phone and say in a really spooky voice, 'Woooo, Kristeee. Phantom here. Woooo, you better hide your plastic ring and your charm necklace, because I'm on my way over . . .' "

I smiled in spite of things. "Well, look. If it *is* the Phantom, we're safe because he probably won't rob the house if someone's in it."

"He might. He has before. Besides, we're just kids. Maybe he figures—"

"He can't figure anything. He doesn't know whether any adults are at home. Just because we answered the phone doesn't mean—"

And at that wonderful moment, the phone rang a third time. I snatched it up, saying, "Hello? . . . Hello?" Then on inspiration, I shouted into the kitchen,

"Hey, Dad, it's another funny call. I think—"

The caller hung up before I could finish saying, "I think we'd better phone the police." I smiled nervously at Kristy as I put the receiver down. She smiled nervously back at me.

"Well," she said briskly, "let's start supper. I bet the kids are hungry."

"Anyone want dinner?" I called into the playroom. Peace was still reigning there. I almost hated to disrupt it. But one of our responsibilities as baby-sitters that night was to feed Jamie and the Feldmans.

"Starving!" Rob shouted, jumping up.

"Yes!" chorused the others. They dropped their crayons and ran.

"Whoa," I said. "Everybody back in the playroom and put the crayons and paper away."

"I wasn't colouring," said Rob.

"You can set the table then," I told him.

"All right," he agreed cheerfully.

A little while later the table was set. Mrs Feldman's sandwiches were stacked on a plate in the middle, the glasses were filled with milk, and Kristy and I were passing round apples and oranges. It was a simple dinner, and everyone, including Kristy and me, seemed happy with it.

In fact, we were so happy that for a few minutes we ate in silence. All I could hear were crunchings and munchings and Jamie gulping his milk.

And a little bang from outside.

My eyes met Kristy's over the tops of our tunafish sandwiches. *Did you hear anything?* I asked her silently.

"Did you hear something?" Rob asked at that moment.

"Oh, probably just the wind," I replied, but my voice was shaking.

"There's no wind tonight," he said.

Another bang, not too loud.

"There it is again," he said.

"Maybe some dog is in one of the dustbins," suggested Kristy.

"Uncle Roger's dustbins are plastic."

"Well," I said bravely, "I'll just go and check things." But I hadn't gone any further than the living room (with Kristy and Rob at my heels), when we distinctly heard noises at one of the front windows and saw a shadow dart away into the falling darkness.

"That does it," I said, suddenly more angry than frightened. "I'm going to call the police."

And I did.

13th CHAPTER

The woman who answered the phone when I dialled 999 was very nice and very helpful. Obviously, she'd been trained to calm down people who were upset.

"Hello, hello!" I said, wishing it were possible to whisper and scream at the same time.

"Yes?" said the woman. "May I help you?"

"I'm baby-sitting," I whispered, "and there's a prowler outside. He was at the front window. We've been getting funny phone calls, too. The kind where the caller hangs up as soon as you answer."

"Okay," she said. "It's a good thing you called. What's your name?"

"Claudia Kishi," I replied.

"And what's the address of the house where you're baby-sitting?"

Thanks to Kristy, I was armed with that

information. It was one of her new safety rules about baby-sitting. Always memorize the address and phone number of your client.

I gave her the address. "Thank you," she said, "and your phone number, too, just in case I need to call you back."

I gave her the number. "Very good. A car is already on its way over. It's just a few streets away and should reach you shortly. In the case of a prowler, though, we don't want to scare him off, so the squad car will park a little distance down the street. Then one officer will search the garden quietly, while the other will come to the door to talk to you."

"Okay," I said, glancing uncertainly outside. It was pretty dark out there. "How will I know it's a policeman at the door?"

"That's a good question. I can tell you're a clever baby-sitter. When the bell rings, ask who's there. The man will identify himself as an officer. Does the door have a chain lock?"

"Yes."

"Slide it shut right now—"

"Kristy, go and put the chain on the front door," I hissed. She ran off.

"—and after the officer has identified himself, open the door just wide enough to see the badge he'll be holding out, okay?"

"Yes," I said. "Thank you. Oh, there's the doorbell. Thanks, thanks," I said hurriedly. I hung up.

Kristy was about to open the door. "Wait," I said, "let me take care of this. The lady told me what to do."

I dashed to the door, aware that Kristy, Rob, Brenda, Rosie, and Jamie had crowded behind me. I was glad. I needed their company.

"Who's there?" I called.

"It's Officer Drew."

After checking to make sure the chain lock was in place, I opened the door a crack. On the Newtons' front door step, bald head glistening under the porch light, stood an elderly man in a policeman's uniform. He looked very nice, kind of like a grandfather, and very official, but he did not look like a policeman. At least, he did not look like my idea of a policeman. However, he was holding out his badge and some kind of I.D., plain as day. I glanced over my shoulder at Kristy. "Psst. Check him out," I whispered. I moved aside and Kristy peered through the crack.

"Who phoned in this—this complaint?" she asked, very businesslike.

"A Claudia Kishi," the man said patiently. "Would that be you?"

"No, it's me," I said from behind Kristy. "It's all right then, Kristy. Let him in."

We opened the door.

And I got the biggest surprise of my life. With the door opened wide, I could see that two people were standing on the path below Officer Drew. One was another cop in uniform.

The other was Alan Gray!

Kristy gasped.

"Who's that?" asked Rob.

Kristy got over her surprise fast, and got ready to battle Alan. After all, they're old enemies. "Alan Gray, you darn, sneaking, rotten—"

"You know this young man?" asked Officer Drew, a smile playing on his lips.

"You bet I do!" cried Kristy. "His name is Alan Gray. He lives in Rockville Court, he's in my year at Stoneybrook Middle School, and he's a—"

Alan's face was falling faster than a ruined souffle.

"That's all right, young lady," said Officer Drew. "I get the general idea."

"Where'd you find him?" I asked.

"Behind the rhododendron bush at the side of the house," replied the other police-man. "By the way, I'm Officer Stanton."

"Hi," said Kristy, Rob, Rosie, Brenda, and I.

"Can I wear your hat?" Jamie asked Officer Drew.

Officer Drew smiled and handed his hat to Jamie. "Could we come in for a minute? I think we have a few things to discuss."

I glanced at Kristy. She was fuming. Her eyes probably could have burned holes right through Alan. "Sure," I said.

Kristy made a face at me.

"Well, I *have* to let them in. They're the po*lice*," I whispered to her, as Jamie and the Feldmans stepped aside to make room for the others.

We all sat down in the living room. "Hey, you guys," I said to our baby-sitting charges, "if you go back in the kitchen now and finish your supper quietly, I'll let you have Cookie Surprises for dessert."

"What are Cookie Surprises?" asked Rob suspiciously.

"If I tell you, they won't be surprises. But you'll find out if you finish your dinner— and stay in the kitchen," I added.

The kids ran back to the kitchen.

Alan, the policeman, Kristy, and I looked at each other.

Officer Drew was about to say something when Kristy let her mouth take over.

"Okay, Alan, spill it," she said. "Was that you at the front window?"

I saw a mischievous glint in Alan's eye, indicating that he was about to say no. Then he glanced up and found Officer Drew and Officer Stanton glaring ferociously at him.

"Yes," he admitted.

"Did you call here three times this afternoon and hang up when Kristy or I answered the phone?" I asked.

Alan dropped his eyes. "Yes."

"You wouldn't, by any chance, have

called me once when I was baby-sitting in McLelland Road, would you?" (That was Watson's house.)

"Yes," he mumbled.

"And a few times here on other days, and maybe once or twice when I was sitting in Rosedale Road?"

"Yes." Alan was whispering by then.

"But how did you know I was going to be at all those places?"

"And why were you harassing this young lady?" said Officer Drew in a tone so stern I practically saluted him. I think he was just trying to frighten Alan a little.

"Well . . . um . . . which question should I answer first?" Alan cautiously asked the policeman.

"Mine," said Kristy.

Officer Stanton raised an eyebrow.

I kicked Kristy on the ankle.

"Okay," Alan licked his lips. "You—you made it easy for me," he said.

"*I* did?" replied Kristy. "How?"

"Well, it was all right there in that notebook of yours."

"What notebo—You mean, our club *record* book?"

"I suppose so. That thing you started bringing to school every day. I checked it each morning. It had all sorts of information in it. Times, addresses—"

Kristy slapped the heel of her hand against her forehead, "—and phone numbers," she finished for Alan.

He nodded.

"Alan, you are a *rat*!" she exploded.

(The vague rustlings and eating sounds from the kitchen stopped suddenly.)

"A huge, gigantic, smelly—"

"All right, simmer down, young lady," said Officer Drew. He turned to Alan. "How did you get hold of the book every morning?"

"I would . . . borrow it. From Kristy's desk when she wasn't looking. I mean, the book was so neat and easy to read."

(Thanks to Mary Anne.)

"Do you know that that was an invasion of privacy?" asked the officer.

"Well. . . ."

"Okay, okay, okay," said Kristy. "So you looked in the book. How come you wanted to scare me?"

"Well," said Alan again, "I didn't. I wanted to—to ask you something, but I just couldn't . . . I didn't have the nerve. And I *couldn't* ask you in school."

"But you had the nerve to steal our book and spy on me, not to mention pull my hair, trip me, take my lunch, and make up stories about me to tell Mr Peters."

"Son," said Officer Stanton in a more kindly voice, "what did you want to ask her?"

Alan mumbled something that nobody could understand.

"Louder!" shouted Rob from the kitchen.

"Finish your sandwich!" I yelled back.

"What, Alan?" asked Kristy, sounding nearly civil.

"I wanted to know if you'd go to the Hallowe'en Hop with me."

If I were Kristy, my eyeballs would have fallen out of my head along about then. But Kristy just said, "Oh, gosh, is *that* all? Of course I'll go with you . . . Thanks."

And at that moment, the Feldmans and the Newtons returned. They were home early.

14th CHAPTER

Needless to say, the grown-ups were pretty surprised to walk into the living room and find their baby-sitters talking to two policemen and a strange boy.

Mrs Newton gasped and Officer Drew jumped up and helped her into a chair. "It's all right, ma'am," he said. "The girls had a little problem, but they handled it well. The children are fine."

"Thank goodness."

"They're in the kitchen eating dinner," I added.

Officer Drew was eyeing Mrs Newton's round belly warily. "Are you sure you're okay, ma'am?" he asked her.

"Just fine," she said breathlessly, "but Claudia, Kristy, what happened here?"

I looked at Kristy, hoping she'd want to explain. "He's *your* boyfriend," I whispered.

280

"*You* were the one who called the police."

I took a slow breath. Mrs Feldman had gone into the kitchen to check the kids, but Mr and Mrs Newton and Mr Feldman were all ears. "Well," I began, "we got three strange phone calls after you left. We'd pick up the phone and the caller wouldn't say anything. And that was what happened to the Goldmans before they were robbed last night. Then, during dinner, we heard noises outside and when we went into the living room, someone was at the window. So I called the police."

"You did the right thing," said Mrs Newton. "That was very responsible of you."

"Except that the prowler turned out to be *him*," I jerked my head toward Alan, "spying on Kristy."

"Well, you didn't know that," said Mr Newton.

"I guess we'd better go now," Officer Drew said, standing up. "Let me just get my hat." At that moment, Jamie ran into the living room and handed it to him. "Thank you, young man. And *you*"—the officer turned to Alan—"are coming with us."

Alan turned pale. He swallowed noisily. "I am?"

"Is he in trouble?" asked Kristy.

"No, we're just going to give him a lift home. On the way, we'll have a chat about

281

privacy and the proper use of the telephone. He can consider this a warning."

"Yes, sir," said Alan. As he followed the policemen out the front door, he glanced over his shoulder. "See you in school tomorrow, Kristy. 'Bye Claudia."

" 'Bye," we said.

"Was he a bad boy, Kristy?" asked Jamie as soon as the door had closed.

"Just a little bit bad," replied Kristy.

"Hey, do we get Cookie Surprises or what?" Rob called to me from the kitchen.

Kristy and I fixed the kids the dessert I had promised—chocolate-chip cookies with little scoops of ice cream on them. Then it was time to leave. Since it was dark, Mr Newton offered to drive us, but we live so close by that we said we'd walk. Besides, I wanted to talk to Kristy.

"So?" I said, when we reached the pavement.

"What?"

"Are you out of your mind? For years, you've hated Alan Gray. Hated his guts. You said so just a few weeks ago. And all we've been hearing since school started last month is how Alan's sitting behind you is about as unfortunate as . . . as . . ."

"As when they moved *The Love Boat* to a.m. so we couldn't watch the re-runs any more?"

"Yeah."

"I know. Well, it's just that Alan finally

proved something my mother's been telling me for years. Only I didn't believe her until now."

"What's that?"

"That boys tease you because they like you. I have to admit that sometimes I still think Alan is kind of a jerk, and I wouldn't have minded if he'd got into a *little* trouble tonight. I mean, hanging round the window and frightening us with those phone calls . . . He deserves to sweat, just like we did. However—Claudia, *a boy likes me*." Kristy paused, then looking mystified, went on, "Besides, he is sort of cute. And I guess some of the things he's done were funny . . . if you look at them a certain way."

I grinned at her. "Now you see how Stacey and I feel. That's why we sit at the lunch table with the boys. They like us. At least, they don't hate us. And it's pretty nice to be asked to a dance, isn't it?"

Kristy nodded, looking confused. "I don't quite understand all this," she said slowly. "I mean, how am I going to explain it to Mary Anne? And, oh, gosh, can you imagine what my brothers will do when they see me getting ready to go to a *dance*?"

"Well, you can't back out now. Look, two nights from now, it will all be over. I think Mary Anne will understand. And Stacey and I will help you get ready before the dance. So don't worry."

We had reached our houses. "Thanks,

Claudia," said Kristy. "I'll see you to-morrow."

" 'Bye." I sounded a lot more cheerful than I felt. As I crossed the street, all I could think was that Emily and Dorianne were going to the Hallowe'en Hop, Stacey was probably going to the Hallowe'en Hop (even though it would be with Pete Black, not Sam Thomas), Mary Anne didn't care about the Hallwe'en Hop and now Kristy was going to the Hallowe'en Hop. And I wasn't. The boy I wished I could go to the Hallowe'en Hop with didn't know anything about me, except that I had once dropped a plate of jelly in his lap.

I opened the front door to my house, let myself in, said hello to Mimi and my parents, and went to my room. I closed the door and lay down on my bed. Planning on being depressed for a while, I pulled a piece of toffee out of the stash in my pencil jar.

I was chewing away thoughtfully when someone knocked on my door. I didn't really want to talk to anyone, except maybe Mimi.

"Who is it?" I yelled.

"Janine."

Groan, groan. I wanted to talk to Janine less than I wanted to talk to a snake. "I can't talk now!"

"I think we'd better. This is urgent."

"Oh, all right. Come in." (Mimi would have been proud of me.)

Janine slipped into my room, closed the door quietly behind her, and perched at the foot of my bed. "What were the police doing at the Newtons'?" she asked me.

I popped another piece of toffee in my mouth before I had finished the first one. "Tap dancing," I managed to say.

"*Claudia* . . ."

"How'd you know they were there?"

"Mrs Gordon was giving me a lift home from the university and I saw the squad car driving away. I didn't think it could be too serious. There were no flashing lights. But I didn't tell Mum and Dad."

"You didn't?" I asked, feeling somewhat amazed. It's not that Janine is a tell-tale, just that it's unlike her to be imaginative enough to think I might be in some kind of trouble that I wanted to cover up.

"No," Janine shook her head.

"Well, thanks," I said. "I mean, it's okay if they know. I'm going to tell them about it in a little while. But thank you for waiting to talk to me first."

Janine smiled and spread her hands, as if to say, No problem —which of course she wouldn't have said, not being one to use slang if she could help it.

"What did happen?" she asked. "Will you tell me first?"

"Sure," I said enthusiastically, sitting up. "Would you like a piece of toffee?" Remembering what Mimi had told me, I planned on making the most out of that sisterly, but unusual, moment.

"All right," said Janine.

I handed her a peppermint piece, and began telling her about Alan. "So then," I said, "I snuck—"

"Sneaked."

"—Whatever—into the living room, and someone was at the window!"

"What did you *do*?" she asked, her dark eyes shining.

"I called the police."

"You didn't scream?"

"Nope. Just went to the telephone." I told her the rest of the story.

"Gosh, you certainly were brave," Janine said appreciatively.

"I guess so," I replied. "I didn't feel brave at the time, though. I just knew that Kristy and I had to protect the children."

"I'm really proud of you."

"You are?"

"Yes. I'm proud you're my sister."

"Wow, I—Thanks . . . Janine?"

"What?"

"How come you don't come to my room and talk to me like this more often?"

"Because you usually tell me to shut up or go away or mind my own business."

"Well, that's because you usually start talking like some big show-off professor. When we were little, we used to have fun. You talked like a kid."

Janine frowned. "Am I talking like a professor now?"

"No. But . . . you're always telling me all this stuff I don't want to know, like how the fear process works. Who cares?"

"I do. Those things are interesting to me."

"Not to me."

"What is interesting to you?" asked Janine.

"Oh, mysteries and scary stories and baby-sitting and painting."

Janine nodded. "What happened tonight was exciting."

"Yeah!"

"I'm glad you let me come in and talk."

"Me, too," I said.

"Maybe we could do this more often?" Janine sounded a bit timid.

"Sure. I have a lot of other sweets hidden round my room."

Janine smiled. "I'll tell you a secret. I do, too."

"You *do*?"

"Mm-hmmm. It's my vice."

I wasn't sure what a vice was, but I wasn't about to ask. "I didn't know that."

"There are a lot of things you don't know about me."

"Same here."

"Well, let's go tell Mum and Dad what happened."

"Okay."

So we did. Mum and Dad and Mimi were pretty proud, too. After that, Janine gave me one final revision for the maths test the next day. She didn't seem to annoy me as much as usual.

Everything was fine until I got into bed. Then I thought of two things that made me feel sort of chilly all over. The first was that Trevor hadn't asked me to the dance.

The second was much worse. If Alan had been making the scary calls to Kristy over the past couple of weeks, then who had been making the calls to me? I'd had them several different times when I'd been baby-sitting, and the Phantom was still at large ... Was it possible, just possible, that he was after *me*?

No, I decided a few seconds later. It wasn't very likely at all. The Phantom went after jewellery, not people. And especially not people who didn't have any jewellery. How would Nancy Drew think if this were a mystery and she were the sleuth? I wondered. She would analyse the clues. She would review all her information.

Well, I thought, Kristy had received mysterious phone calls. I had received mysterious phone calls. Kristy's caller turned out to be Alan, a boy who secretly liked her. Maybe my caller was a boy, too! After all, Alan had looked in our record book. Maybe he had shown it to someone else.

Who could have a crush on me? Rick

Chow? Maybe. Howie? I needed more clues.

I rolled over on my side and fell asleep.

The awful mystery was cleared up the next afternoon on what turned out to be a red-letter day. First, I took the maths test. I worked very carefully and was the last person to turn my test in. I wasn't sure how well I'd done, but I knew I had tried my best, which is not something I can say often.

But, boy, was I surprised when Mr Peters found me at my locker at the end of the school day and said, "Congratulations, Claudia!"

"On what?" I asked warily.

"I started grading the test papers at lunch today. Yours was on top. I thought you'd like to know that you got an eighty-six."

"Really? An eighty-*six*? What is that, a 'B'?"

"A 'B' or a 'B-plus', depending on how the rest of the class does. I can tell you've been working hard. It's really showing. Keep it up."

"I will, oh, I *will*! Thank you!"

As if that weren't enough excitement, I was baby-sitting for Nina and Eleanor Marshall a couple of hours later when the phone rang. I picked it up nervously.

No one was there.

"*Darn*," I said, as I replaced the receiver.

"What?" asked Nina.

"Oh, just a—a wrong number." Was it my secret caller? I actually began to hope the phone would ring again!

Immediately, it did. I grabbed up the receiver. "Hello? Who is this? Say something, *please*!" I waited, and after a moment an unfamiliar male voice said, "Claudia?"

I caught my breath. "Y-yes?"

The voice cleared his throat. "Um, this—this is Trevor. Trevor Sandbourne."

I very nearly fainted. "Nina," I whispered placing my hand over the mouthpiece, "go and get out the Sesame Street Puzzles. I'll help you and Eleanor with them in a few minutes." I uncovered the phone as Nina and Eleanor ran off. "Trevor?" I said. I couldn't believe it!

"Yes. You . . . know who I am?"

"Oh, yes. I mean, of course I do. You're the poet. You write for *The Literary Voice*."

"That's right," he said shyly. "What I was wondering is—I mean, I know this is last-minute, but could you—would like to go to the Hallowe'en Hop with me?"

This wasn't happening. It couldn't be. In a few minutes, I would wake up and find that the phone call was just part of a very real dream, like Dorothy's trip to Oz.

I pinched myself. It hurt. "I'd like to, Trevor. Thanks."

"You mean you can go?"

"Yes."

290

"Oh, good. I'll meet you there . . . at the dance. Tomorrow at four, okay?"

"Okay. Trevor?" (I had to ask him.) "How did you know where to reach me? This isn't my house."

There was a pause at Trevor's end of the phone. "I sort of found out from Alan Gray."

"Aha."

"I—I know you know about Alan and the baby-sitting book. And, see, every time Alan took it, he'd check to see where Kristy'd be sitting . . . and then he would write down where *you'd* be sitting and give me the information. He knew I liked you. He caught me writing a poem about us once."

"A poem? About us?"

"Yeah . . ."

"Do you still have it?"

"No," said Trevor sheepishly. "I threw it away. I was so embarrassed. Alan started singing some dumb song about kissing in a tree. Everybody heard him."

"So *that's* how he found out," I said.

"Yeah. Well, he felt bad about teasing me, since we're friends, so he began looking up your appointments for me. It was just his way of apologizing . . . I guess now I owe *you* an apology. I'm really sorry, Claudia. Alan told me what happened last night. He didn't want me to get into trouble, so he didn't mention my name in front of the police. But when he got home, he phoned me and said I'd better straighten things out with you, no matter how sh—how hard it is for me. I'm sorry I've scared you with the phone calls. I really like you. I've been noticing you all year. I was just afraid to talk to you."

"That's all right, Trevor. I'm glad you finally did. I like you, too. I'll see you tomorrow."

I hung up the phone. I was going to the Hallowe'en Hop after all! What a day!

"Hey, girls!" I called to Nina and Eleanor. "We're going to celebrate. Get your coats. I'll treat you to ice-cream cones!"

So we celebrated. We celebrated the happiest day of my life.

15th
CHAPTER

The Hallowe'en Hop was terrific. Kristy and Alan were there, and so were Stacey and Pete. Stacey looked as if she were having fun. Maybe Pete would help her forget about Sam Thomas. Mary Anne didn't go, and seemed quite happy about it.

On Thursday night, the night before the dance, Stacey and Kristy and I ran round to each of our houses as a group, trying on outfits for the others to approve. We had made a unanimous decision not to go in costume. We wanted to look nice. Besides, the boys had said they wouldn't be caught dead in costumes. Stacey and I ended up with baggy jeans and new bulky sweaters. We couldn't talk Kristy out of a pinafore dress jumper and red turtleneck, but the next day, Alan didn't seem to care. When we got to the school gymnasium (after dashing home, changing out of our school clothes and into

293

our dance clothes, then dashing back), Alan met Kristy with a grin on his face that was as big as the ones on Trevor and Pete's faces.

After I hung up my coat, Trevor and I stood at the punch table and laughed about his phone calls and the jelly accident. When we ran out of things to talk about, we danced. To be honest, Trevor isn't much of a dancer and neither am I, but we had fun— lots of fun—anyway.

I had a new friend.

On the Monday after Hallowe'en, Mr Peters handed back our maths tests. My eighty-six had worked out to a 'B-plus'. I gave my family the good news at dinner that night.

"Bravo!" said Dad.

"I'm so proud," said Mum.

Janine got up and actually gave me a little hug.

And Mimi smiled gravely and said, "I knew you could do it, my Claudia."

Two days later, the police caught the Phantom Caller—for real. They caught him in the act. A Mr and Mrs Johnson Neustetter, who lived in a house in Mercer that was more like a palace, got two of the Phantom's phone calls on Wednesday afternoon. The Neustetters had been following the accounts of the Phantom in the news, and alerted the police. On a hunch, the police staked out the Neustetters' that night. They arranged for the Neustetters to go out (figuring the Phantom was watching the house from somewhere). Sure enough, about twenty minutes after they'd left, the Phantom showed up. The police let him get into the house and all the way into Mr Neustetter's safe before surprising him. He confessed to everything.

That night the Phantom was behind bars.

But guess whose mystery didn't get solved? The Goldmans'. The Phantom said he'd never been in Stoneybrook. So the police decided the Goldmans really had been robbed by a copycat thief. With the Phantom behind bars, though, no one would try that again. It would be too risky.

With that news, Mary Anne was back in the Babysitters Club. As soon as she and her father heard the news, Mary Anne begged to be allowed to baby-sit again and her father gave in.

We celebrated the capture of the Phantom at our next club meeting. I was ready with lemonade, a big bag of potato crisps, another of peanuts, and an apple and a packet of crackers for Stacey.

"Well," said Kristy, tipping her head back and getting ready to drop a handful of peanuts into her mouth, "we survived the Phantom Caller."

"Yeah," I said. "This club can do anything."

"I've earned sixteen dollars in the last two weeks," said Stacey.

"I earned fourteen," added Kristy.

I opened up four tins of diet lemonade and handed them round.

"Here's to success," said Stacey.

"To us," said Mary Anne.

"To the Phantom," said Kristy, giggling.

"Here's to the Babysitters Club!" I cried.

We grinned, and clinked our tins.

THE TRUTH
ABOUT STACEY

Book 3

THE TRUTH
ABOUT STACEY

1st
CHAPTER

"As chairman of the Babysitters Club," said Kristy Thomas, "I hereby move that we decide what to do when Mrs Newton goes to the hospital to have her baby."

"What do you mean?" I said.

"Well, we ought to be prepared. We've been waiting for this baby for months, and the Newtons are practically our best clients. They'll need someone to take care of Jamie while his parents are at the hospital. Clever baby-sitters would be ready for the occasion."

"I think that's a good idea," spoke up Mary Anne Spier. "I second the motion." Mary Anne usually agrees with Kristy. After all, they're best friends.

I glanced across the room at Claudia Kishi. Claudia is *my* best friend, and vice-chairman of our club. She shrugged her shoulders at me.

There are just the four of us in the Baby-sitters Club: Kristy, Claudia, Mary Anne (she's the secretary), and me, Stacey McGill. I'm the treasurer. We've been in business for about two months. Kristy thought up the club, which was why she became chairman. We meet three times a week from five-thirty to six o'clock in Claudia's room (Claudia has a private phone), and our clients call then to line us up as sitters. The reason the club works so well is that with four baby-sitters there at the phone, each person who calls is pretty much guaranteed to get a sitter for whatever time he or she needs. Our clients like that. They say that having to make a whole bunch of calls just to line up one sitter is a waste of time. They like us, too. We're good baby-sitters. And we worked hard to get our business going. We printed up fliers and put them through letterboxes, and even put an ad in *The Stoneybrook News*, the voice of Stoneybrook, Connecticut.

That's where I live now, in this teeny-weeny town in Connecticut. Let me tell you, it's quite a shock after life in New York City. New York is a big place. Stoneybrook is not. There is only one middle school here, and I go to it. We all do. (We're in seventh grade.) In New York there are about a billion middle schools. In fact, in New York there are about a billion of everything — people, cars, buildings, stores, pigeons, friends, and things to do.

Here there's, well, there's . . . not much, really. My parents and I moved into our house in August and I didn't make a single friend until I met Claudia in school in September. Everyone here seems to have known everyone else since they were babies. Claudia, Kristy, and Mary Anne have. And they've grown up together, since Kristy and Mary Anne live next door to each other on Bradford Court and Claudia lives across the street from them. (I live two streets away.)

So, was I glad when Claudia told me Kristy wanted to start the club! Friends at last, I thought. And that's just what I found. Even though I'm better friends with Claudia, I don't know what I'd do without Kristy and Mary Anne. It's true that they seem younger than Claudia and me (they don't care much about clothes or boys yet— although Kristy *did* just go to her first dance), and Mary Anne is unbelievably shy, and Kristy's sort of a tomboy. But they're my friends, and I belong with them. Which is more than I can say about certain traitors I left behind in New York.

"All right, here's one plan," Kristy was saying. "It's a school afternoon. Mrs Newton realizes that it's time to go to the hospital. She calls Mr Newton or a cab or whatever, then calls us, and one of us goes to stay with Jamie."

"What if we're all busy?" I asked.

"Hmm," said Kristy. "Maybe from now on, one of us should be free each afternoon so Mrs Newton will be guaranteed a baby-sitter. It will be a special service for her, since the Newtons are such good customers."

"That seems like kind of a waste," spoke up Claudia, which was exactly what I was thinking.

"That's right," I said. "Babies can be late. Two or three weeks late. We could be giving up an awful lot of perfectly good afternoons for nothing."

"That's true," said Kristy thoughtfully.

"How about a night-time plan?" I suggested. "Doesn't it seem that pregnant women always rush off to the hospital in the middle of the night? I was born at 2.22 am."

"I was born at 4.36 am." said Claudia.

"I was born at 4 am on the dot," said Kristy.

We looked at Mary Anne. She shrugged. "I don't know what time I was born." Mary Anne's mother died when Mary Anne was little, and Mary Anne is not very close to her strict father. It figures that they'd never talked about the day (or night) she was born.

A knock came on Claudia's door. Mimi, her grandmother, stuck her head in the room. "Hello, girls," she said politely.

"Hi, Mimi," we answered

"May I offer you something to eat?" she asked. Claudia's family is Japanese, and

Mimi, who didn't come to the United States until she was thirty-two years old, speaks with a gentle rolling accent. She has lived with Claudia's family since before Claudia was born.

"No thanks, Mimi," replied Claudia, "but maybe you could help us."

"Certainly." Mimi opened the door the rest of the way and stood just inside the room.

"Do you know what time Mary Anne was born?" Claudia asked. She figured Mimi would know since Claudia's parents have been friendly with the Thomases and the Spiers for years, and Mimi had got to know the families, too.

Mimi looked only slightly take aback. "Let me think for a moment, my Claudia. . . . Mary Anne, your mother and father left for the hospital around dinner-time. That I remember clearly. I believe you were born about eleven o'clock."

"Oh!" A grin lit up Mary Anne's face. "I didn't know. So I was another night-time baby. Thank you, Mimi."

"It was my pleasure." Mimi turned to leave, and almost bumped into Janine, Claudia's sister, who had come up behind her.

"Claudia! Claudia!" cried Janine.

I looked up in alarm. Janine is this prim, not-much-fun fifteen-year-old who's a genius. To be honest, she's boring. Dull as dishwater. I'd never even heard her raise her voice, which was why, the minute I heard her cry, "Claudia!" I knew something was wrong. Very wrong.

Unfortunately, I was right.

"Janine! What is it?" exclaimed Claudia.

"This." Janine was waving a paper around. She squeezed past Mimi and thrust it at Claudia.

Claudia took it and Kristy, Mary Anne, and I crowded around. We stared at the paper in horror. This is what we saw:

The four of us just looked at each other. Even Kristy, who has sort of a big mouth, couldn't say anything. Mary Anne's eyes grew so wide I though they would pop right out of her head.

"What is wrong, my Claudia?" asked Mimi.

"Competition," Claudia replied stiffly.

Kristy checked her watch and saw that it was only five forty-five, and that we still had fifteen minutes left to our Friday meeting. "I hereby change this meeting of the Babysitters Club to an emergency meeting," she announced.

"We will leave you alone, then," said Mimi softly. "Janine, please help me with dinner." Mimi tiptoed out, followed by Janine, who closed the door softly behind her.

I looked at my three stricken friends.

Claudia's dark eyes were troubled. She was absentmindedly playing with a strand of her long black hair. Claudia is very fashion-conscious and always dresses in the most trendy clothes, but I could tell that clothes were the last thing on her mind.

Kristy, wearing her typical little-girl clothes, her brown hair pulled back into a messy ponytail, looked as troubled as Claudia did.

Mary Anne, her hair in plaits as usual (her father makes her wear it that way), had put on her wire-rimmed glasses to read the flier. When she was finished, she sighed, leaned back against the wall, and kicked off her shoes.

If I could have looked at myself, I would have seen a second trendy dresser and a fourth long face, more sophisticated than Kristy's or Mary Anne's, but not nearly as beautiful as Claudia's.

I examined a pink-painted nail while Kristy held the dreadful flier in her shaking hand.

"We're dead," she said to no one in particular. "The other baby-sitters are older than we are. They can stay out later than we can. We're doomed."

Not one of us disagreed with her.

In nervous desperation, Claudia took a shoe box from under her bed, reached in, and pulled out a pack of chewing gum. Claudia is a junk-food addict (although she won't admit it) and she has sweets and snacks stashed all around her bedroom, along with the Nancy Drew books her parents disapprove of because they think they're not "quality" reading. She was so upset about the Baby-sitters Agency that when she was passing around the chewing gum, she forgot and offered *me* a piece. I'm diabetic and absolutely not allowed to eat extra sweets. I used to try to keep my illness a secret from people, but Claudia, Mary Anne, and Kristy know about it, and they don't usually offer me sweets.

"Who *are* Liz Lewis and Michelle Patterson?" asked Mary Anne, peering over to look at the flier again.

I shrugged. I barely knew the kids in my classroom, let alone in any other grade.

"Maybe they don't go to the middle school," suggested Kristy. "It says the baby-sitters are thirteen and up. Liz and Michelle probably go to the high school. I wonder if Sam or Charlie know them." (Charlie and Sam are Kristy's older brothers. They're sixteen and fourteen. She has a little brother, too, David Michael, who's six.)

"No, they go to Stoneybrook Middle School," spoke up Claudia, in a tone of voice that indicated she was likely to expire in a few seconds. "They're eighth-graders."

"They must be pretty friendly with the high school kids," I said, "unless there are a whole bunch of really old eighth-graders that we don't know about."

Claudia snorted. "For all I know, there are. Liz and Michelle could be fourteen or fifteen. I wish you guys knew who they are. You'd faint. Those two aren't baby-sitters any more than I'm the Queen of France."

"What's wrong with them?" I asked.

"For one thing, I wouldn't trust them further than I could throw a truck," said Claudia. "They have smart mouths, they cheek the teachers, they hate school, they hang around at the mall. You know, *that*

310

kind of kid."

"It doesn't mean they're not good baby-sitters," said Mary Anne.

"I'd be surprised if they were," said Claudia.

"I wonder how the agency works," mused Kristy. She was still holding the flier. "There are only two names on this, but it says you can get in touch with 'a whole network of responsible baby-sitters.' I'll say one thing, Liz and Michelle know how to go after customers. Their flier is a lot better than ours was."

"Hmph," I said.

"Hey!" cried Mary Anne. "I have an idea. Let's call the agency and pretend we need a sitter. Maybe we can find out how those girls operate." Mary Anne may be shy, but she sure can come up with daring ideas.

"Oh, that's smart!" said Kristy approvingly. "I'll make up a name and say I need a baby-sitter for my younger brother. Then I can call them back later and cancel."

"Okay," Claudia and I agreed.

"Competition, are you ready?" Kristy asked the phone. "Here comes the Babysitters Club!"

2nd
CHAPTER

Kristy called Liz Lewis, just because Liz was listed first on the flier. She put her hand over the mouthpiece. "It's ringing," she whispered to us. "One . . . two . . . thr— Hello? Is Liz Lewis there, please? . . . Oh, hi, Liz. My name is—Candy. Candy Kane. . . . No, no joke. . . I got your flier for the Baby-sitters Agency. I'm supposed to sit for my little brother tomorrow and—" Kristy paused, and the rest of us watched the wheels turning" —I just got asked out on a date."

Mary Anne started to giggle. She grabbed a pillow from Claudia's bed and buried her face in it to muffle the sounds. Kristy turned away so she wouldn't have to see.

"From three to five," Kristy was saying. (Liz must have asked her when she was supposed to be sitting.) "He's seven years old. His name is, um, Harry. . . . Twenty-eight Roper Road. Will *you* be baby-sitting for him? The flier said—Oh, I see. . . . Mm-hmm. . . . I'll be at 52321. Oh, but only for about ten minutes. Then I have—I have another date. . . . Who with?" By that time, Claudia was laughing, too, and I was on the verge of it. Kristy glanced at us helplessly, not sure what to do about her "date." Then she simply pulled a name out of the air. "With Winston Churchill," she replied, taking the chance that Liz wouldn't know who he was. Apparently she didn't. "Yeah, he goes to high school," continued Kristy nonchalantly, getting into her story. "A football player. . . . Me? I'm in seventh. . . . Yeah, I know."

I had to leave the room. I couldn't stand it any longer, and I didn't want to ruin Kristy's call. I closed Claudia's door, ran to the bathroom, laughed, and returned.

Kristy was saying, "Okay, five minutes. . . . Yeah, later." She hung up. Then she began to laugh, too. "You guys!" she exclaimed. "Don't do that to me when I'm on the phone."

"But Winston *Churchill?*" I cried. "The high school guy you're *dating?*"

When we calmed down, Kristy said, "All right, this is how I think the agency works. People call Liz and Michelle when they need sitters. Then Liz and Michelle simply turn around and *find* the sitters. In other words, they do all the phoning for their clients. I guess they must baby-sit, too, from time to time. But when they don't, they probably get part of the salary earned by the sitter they found for the job."

"No wonder their sitters are so old," said Mary Anne. "All Liz and Michelle have to do is *call* older kids."

"Yeah," said Kristy glumly. "We could do that ourselves, if we'd thought of it." She paused. "Liz seemed more interested in my date than in finding a baby-sitter."

"Figures," said Claudia.

The phone rang. "I'll get it. It's probably Liz," said Kristy.

Mary Anne got ready with a pillow.

"Hello, the B—hello?" (Kirsty had almost said, "Hello, the Babysitters Club," which is how we answer the phone during meetings.) "Yes, this is she. . . . Oh, terrific. . . . *How many?* . . . Wow. How old are they? . . . Okay. . . . Patricia Clayton. . . . Okay. . . . Okay, thanks a lot. I'll see Patricia tomorrow. . . . Later." She hung up.

"Later?" repeated Mary Anne.

"That's how Liz says goodbye."

"So?" I asked.

"She actually found three available sitters," said Kristy. "She gave me a choice. I didn't know any of the names, but two were thirteen years old, and one was fifteen years old. One was even a *boy*. I chose the fifteen-year-old. People are going to *love* the agency. I'm not kidding. We don't offer a

314

range of ages like they do. There are no boys in our club. And we can't stay out past ten, even on the weekends."

We looked at each other sadly.

At last Mary Anne stood up. "It's after six. I've got to go home." Mr Spier likes Mary Anne home on the dot. I was surprised she was letting herself be even a few minutes late. It just showed how upset she was.

"I might as well go, too," I said.

"Yeah," said Kristy.

The three of us said goodbye to Claudia and left. "See you guys!" called Mary Anne, when we reached the Kishis' doorstep. She was suddenly in a hurry. Across the street I could see her father standing at their front door.

"Well," I said to Kristy.

"Well."

"Kristy, we'll make it. We're good baby-sitters."

"I know," she said. But that was *all* she said. I kind of expected Kristy to be a little more positive. I mean, the club was really more hers than anybody else's. I thought she'd do anything for the club. I would.

But maybe that was because the club was more than just a project or a business to me. It was my friends. It was the only good thing that had happened to me in the last horrible year.

I ran home.

Somehow, I managed to eat dinner that night. It wasn't easy. For one thing, ever since I developed the diabetes and I've had to watch what I eat so carefully, food simply isn't much fun any more. Often, when I'm hungry, I don't care *what* I eat. I eat just to fill up. And since I was upset about the Baby-sitters Agency that night, I wasn't even hungry. But Mum watches my food intake like a hawk, particularly since I've lost a little weight recently. So I forced down what I thought was a reasonable dinner.

As soon as I could, I escaped to my room. I closed my door and sat down in my armchair to think. It had been just a year earlier that I had started to show the symptoms of diabetes. At first, we didn't think anything was wrong. I was hungry all the time—I mean, *really* hungry, nothing could fill me up—and thirsty, too. "Well, you're a growing girl," Mum had said. "I expect this is the beginning of a growth spurt. Let's measure you." Sure enough, I'd grown an inch and a half. But then, even though I was eating and eating, I began to lose weight. I didn't feel well, either. I grew tired easily and sometimes I felt weak all over. Twice, I wet my bed. (The second time, I happened to be sharing a double bed with my former best friend, Laine

Cummings, when I was staying overnight.) When that happened, Mum forgot about my growth spurt and decided I was having a psychological problem. She took me to a fancy New York psychiatrist. During my first session with him, he asked me about the bed-wetting, heard that I was losing weight, and watched me drink three lemonades. He was the one who realized what was going on and told Mum to make an appointment with my paediatrician. Mum did. Two weeks later I was learning how to give injections, practising on poor defenceless oranges, thinking that, very shortly, those oranges were going to be *me*.

Diabetes is a problem with a gland in your body called the pancreas. The pancreas makes insulin, which is a hormone. What insulin does is use the sugar and starch that your body takes in when you eat, to give you heat and energy and to break down other foods. When the pancreas doesn't make enough insulin to do the job, then glucose from the sugars and starches builds up in your blood and makes you sick. And not just a little sick. If you don't treat diabetes properly, you could *die*.

Well, *I* practically died when I first heard that. But then the doctor explained that you can give yourself injections of insulin every day to keep the right amount in your body. When you take insulin and control your diet, you can lead a normal life. That was why I was learning how to give injections—so that I could inject myself with insulin every day.

Tell me that's not weird. I used to be one of those kids who cried at the very thought of a flu shot. I never even learned how to sew, for fear of pricking my fingers. And then I discover that not only am I going to need shots every day for the rest of my life, but I'm going to have to give them to *myself*. It was almost too much to bear. But what could I do? Mum or Dad could give me the shots, but then I'd be dependent on them. And what about staying with friends or going on field trips—was I supposed to bring one of my parents along? No way. I had to learn to give myself injections. I didn't like it then, and I don't like it now, but it's better than being tied to my parents—or dying. The one thing I will never do, though, is let my new friends in Stoneybrook see me give myself an injection. It's just too awful. And the truth is, every time I give myself one, I feel like a very sick person—just for a few moments. And I never want my friends to think the same thing, whether it's the truth or not.

Before I got diabetes, I really had it pretty easy. I'm an only child. For as long as I could remember, I'd lived in a large flat in a nice, safe building with a doorman on the Upper West Side in New York City. I had my own bedroom with windows that looked out over Central Park. I went to a private school. I didn't have any pets, and, of course, no brothers or sisters, but I wasn't lonely. I had lots of friends at school and in my building, and my parents let me invite them over whenever I wanted. Mum and Dad seemed to be pretty cool parents—a little pushy, maybe, and more involved in my life than I liked, but that was it. They let me dress the way I wanted, go out with my friends after school, and play my stereo at top volume as long as the neighbours didn't complain.

Then, right before I began to get sick, Mum found out that she and Dad couldn't have any more children. They'd been trying for a long time, but they hadn't been able to have a brother or sister for me. It was unfortunate that they got that news just before I got the diabetes. What if I died? I'd be gone and they wouldn't be able to have another child. Suddenly they were faced with the possibility of *no* children—no children of their own, anyway.

That was sad, but the upshot of it was that, practically overnight, Mum and Dad became the world's two most overprotective parents—and not just where food and insulin were concerned. Suddenly, they began to worry about me when I wasn't home. Mum would call me at my friends' flats after school to make sure I was all right. She even called me at school every noon until the headmistress suggested that it wasn't very healthy for me, and reminded Mum about the nice, qualified school nurse.

Then began the business with the doctors. My parents became convinced that they could find either a miracle cure or a better treatment for me. They never doubted that I had diabetes; they just couldn't leave it alone. They made Helping Stacey their new goal in life.

Unfortunately, they weren't helping me at all. I was losing friends fast, and being yanked out of school to see some new doctor every time I turned around didn't make things any better. Laine Cummings began to hate me the night I wet the bed we were sharing. I didn't blame her for being mad, but why did she have to be mad for so long? We'd been best friends since we were five. Laine said that the real reason she was mad was that I had spent a lot of time at the party that night talking to Allison Ritz, a new girl. But I don't know. Laine acted strange after I wet the bed, stranger still the first time I had to stay in the hospital, and even stranger after I started going to all those doctors. Maybe I should have told her about the diabetes, but for some reason, my parents kept the truth a secret from their friends, so I did the same. In fact, I didn't tell anyone the truth until we left New York and started over again in Connecticut. I finally told Claudia, Kristy, and Mary Anne my secret.

But Laine still doesn't know, and even though her parents are my parents' best friends, they don't know, either. I don't see what the big deal is, but I guess it doesn't matter now.

At the beginning of my illness hospital visits couldn't be avoided. I needed tests, I had to have my diet and insulin regulated, and once I fainted at school and went into insulin shock and the ambulance came and took me to St Luke's. If one of my friends got that sick, I would have called her in the hospital and sent her cards and visited her when she went home. But not Laine. She seemed almost afraid of me (although she tried to cover up by acting cool and snooty). And my other friends did what Laine did, because she was the leader. Their leader. My leader. And we were her followers.

The school year grew worse and worse. I fainted twice more at school, each time causing a big scene and getting lots of attention, and every week, it seemed, I missed at least one morning while Mum and Dad took me to some doctor or clinic or other. Laine called me a baby, a liar, a hypochondriac, and a lot of other things that indicated she thought my parents and I were making a big deal over nothing.

But if she *really* thought it was nothing, why wouldn't she come over to my flat any more? Why wouldn't she share sandwiches or go to the movies with me? And why did she move her desk away from mine in school? I was confused and unhappy and sick, and I didn't have any friends left, thanks to Laine.

I hated Laine.

In June, Mum and Dad announced that we were moving to Connecticut. I didn't have any friends there, but I didn't have any left in New York, either, so what did it matter? They said they were moving because Dad wanted to transfer to a different branch of the company he worked for, but somehow I knew they were moving partly because of me—to get me out of the city, away from the sooty air and the dirt and the noise, away from all the bad times and bad memories. They were overreacting and I knew it.

But I didn't care.

3rd
CHAPTER

I might have continued to moon away all evening, except that my thoughts (all by themselves) suddenly turned to something much more interesting: boys. All boys are pretty interesting, but I like two in particular. One is Kristy's brother, Sam. He's the one who's fourteen, a first year at Stoneybrook High. I know he liked *me* the first time we met. I was baby-sitting for Kristy's little brother, and Sam came home, and his jaw nearly fell off his face when he saw me in the kitchen. I thought he was cute, too, and my own jaw nearly fell off. We had fun together that day, but not much has happened since. I don't know why. I look exactly the same, I haven't done anything to offend him, and although I go over to Kristy's sometimes, hoping to see Sam, I never annoy him. Maybe I'm just too young for him.

I don't worry about him much, though. I have a sort of boyfriend in my own grade now. His name is Pete Black. He and I had been sitting at the same lunch table with Claudia, and the other kids in the group she introduced me to—Dori, Emily, Rick, and Howie—since almost the beginning of school, but nothing special had happened with Pete until a couple of weeks ago when he asked me to go to the Hallowe'en Hop with him. Of course I said yes, and we went and had a wonderful time. Now we always sit next to each other in the cafeteria, and some evenings, Pete phones me just to talk.

"Knock, knock," called a voice from the other side of my bedroom door.

Mum.

I didn't really feel like talking to her.

"Can I come in?" she asked.

"Okay."

"Honey, are you feeling all right?" She asked the question even before she sat down on my bed.

"Yes. Fine." I hear the question about ten times a day.

"You didn't eat much dinner tonight."

"I wasn't hungry."

Mum began to look panicked. "You didn't have a snack over at Claudia's, did you?"

"*Mother*. Of course not." The thing is, I am allowed a certain amount of sweet stuff each day. In fact, I *have* to eat a certain amount of sweets in order to maintain that delicate balance between food and insulin. My diet is so exact, though, that I can't just have a snack whenever I feel like it. I can't, for instance, suddenly decide to eat a bar of chocolate or something over at Claudia's, and then make up for it by giving myself extra insulin. It just doesn't work. In fact, it's a good way to make myself sick. So you can see why Mum panicked at the thought of my having a snack. But for heaven's sake, doesn't she trust me? *I* don't want to get sick, either. "Honey, I was just asking. . . . Are you really feeling fine?"

"*Yes*."

"But you've lost three pounds."

"I can't help it. Maybe I'm more active now that I have some friends. Maybe we need to increase my diet."

"Are you hungry all the time?"

"Not all the time. Not like I was before we knew I had diabetes. But sometimes it seems like an awfully long time from one meal to the next."

"You weren't hungry tonight, though."

"No. . . ." I didn't want to talk about the Babysitters Club.

"Well, I'll call the doctor on Monday."

"Which one?" My main doctor, the specialist my paediatrician sent me to when the diabetes was first discovered, is in New York. Her name is Dr Werner. But of course I have to have a doctor here in

Stoneybrook, too, so Dr Werner referred us to Dr Frank. Both doctors are nice, but I like Dr Werner better.

"I'll call Dr Frank, I guess," said Mum. "I don't think we need to bother Dr Werner."

I nodded.

Mum opened her mouth to say something, then closed it, hesitating. After a few more silent seconds she said, "Just so you're prepared, dear—"

I cringed. Whatever was coming didn't sound good.

"—I want you to know that you're going to be scheduled for a series of tests with a new doctor in New York at the beginning of December."

I groaned.

"He's someone Uncle Eric heard about on a television programme."

"We're going to a doctor because Uncle Eric saw him on TV?" I exclaimed.

"Honey, supposedly he's working miracles with diabetes. After Uncle Eric saw him, I found two articles about him in medical journals, and then *Profiles* magazine did a long interview with him. It was very impressive. He's getting a lot of attention right now."

"Did Dr Werner say we should go see him?"

"No."

"Dr Frank?"

326

"No."

"Have you even discussed this with them?"

"No."

"But Mum, *why*? Why do I have to see another new doctor? There's no way to treat what I've got except with the diet and the insulin, and that's just what we're doing."

"There are always new developments, Stacey," said Mum quietly. "Your father and I want the best for you."

"We've *got* the best."

"It's only for three days."

"Three days! Three *days*? Do you know how much school I'll miss? And it'll all be for nothing. It always is. I spent sixth grade falling further and further behind, trying to keep up. Now I've started over in a new place, away from New York City, and you're going to keep dragging me back there and ruining my life? Mum, it's not fair."

"Hey, hey, hey. What's going on here?" Dad poked his head in my door.

"The doctors, Dad. More doctors. I don't mind going to New York to see Dr Werner, but don't make me keep looking for a miracle. Miracles don't happen. If *you* want to look, fine, but don't make me search with you."

"Young lady," said my father, "I don't appreciate your tone of voice."

I didn't answer him.

327

"We're doing this because we love you," said Mum.

"I know."

"We want what's best for you," added Dad.

"I *know*."

"All right." Dad sounded tired.

"I'll tell you about the new doctor some other time," said Mum. My parents left the room.

As soon as they closed the door I heard the phone ring. A few seconds later, Dad called, "Stacey! For you."

"Coming!" I shouted.

I picked up the extension in my parents' bedroom, since Mum and Dad were downstairs. "Hello?" Half of me hoped the caller was Pete. The other half hoped for Sam Thomas.

It was Kristy. "Hi," she said glumly. "I've been thinking."

"Oh, good! About the club, I hope."

"What else? We didn't get nearly enough done at our meeting this afternoon. I think we need to hold a special planning session."

"Great idea. I'll do anything for the club."

"Hey, thanks!" said Kristy. She sounded slightly less grim.

"Sure, I said. "I don't want anything to happen to the club." Oh, boy. If she only knew how *badly* I didn't want anything to happen to it.

328

"Tomorrow morning, eleven o'clock, club headquarters," said Kristy. (The club headquarters, of course, are in Claudia's bedroom.)

"I'll see you then," I said. We hung up.

I thought about our club problem for a long time before I fell asleep that night.

The next day, Kristy was running in high gear. I'd never seen her so keyed-up. For one thing, instead of sprawling on the floor the way she usually did during a meeting, she took over Claudia's desk, sitting up very tall in the straight-backed chair. For another thing, she was wearing a visor. And she was holding a clipboard and had stuck a pencil over her ear.

Mary Anne, who was perched in a director's chair, exchanged glances with Claudia and me on the bed. I could tell that Mary Anne and Claudia wanted to laugh at Kristy's overzealousness. But for some reason, I didn't.

"All right, the meeting will come to order," said Kristy brusquely. Mary Anne and Claudia calmed down. I gave my full attention to Kristy.

"Now," she began, one foot tapping insistently against a chair leg, "I've drawn up a list of ways to improve ourselves as baby-sitters and make us look better to our clients.

"Number one, we will do housework at

329

no extra charge. Our clients will get the benefits of mother's helpers at baby-sitters' prices."

Claudia groaned. "I *hate* housework."

"Do you want to start losing jobs to Liz and Michelle?" Kristy asked her crisply.

"No," grumbled Claudia.

"Number two," continued Kristy, "we will offer special deals to our best customers."

I nodded my head vigorously.

"Number three, we will each make up a 'Kid-Kit' to bring with us when we sit."

"What's a 'Kid-Kit'?" asked Claudia.

"I was just about to explain," said Kristy. "It's something that will not only make us look like dedicated baby-sitters to the parents, but will be really fun for the kids. You know how you like to go over to your friends' houses because your friends always seem to have better stuff than you do? Better food, better things to do, and—when you were little—better toys?"

"Oh, yes!" I exclaimed. "In New York I had this friend named Laine. I loved to go to her apartment because her mother would buy Milky Way bars and keep them in the freezer. Biting into one of those was like biting into a frozen chocolate milk sha—"

I broke off, realizing that Claudia, Kristy, and Mary Anne was staring at me.

"Oh, well, that was *before* I got sick," I added. "Anyway, I know what you mean."

"Yeah," said Mary Anne. "I like Kristy's house because of her big family and Louie." (Louie is the Thomases' collie.)

"When I was a kid, I liked your house, Claud, because of all those board games you used to have," said Kristy, smiling. "Anyway what we really like is the change of pace—new things or different things. So I thought, what better way to make a kid happy than to bring him some new things? Not *really* new, but new to the kid, and not to keep, of course, just to play with while we're there. The kids will *want us* to baby-sit because we'll be like a walking toy store. They probably won't even want us to leave, which should look good to the parents.

"See, what each of us will do is decorate a box and label it 'Kid-Kit'. When we're going to sit somewhere, we'll fill it with games, toys, and books of our own, plus some things like paper and crayons that we'll have to replace from time to time. We can pay for them with our club subs. Then we'll each bring the kit along with us. The kids will love it."

"Great idea!" I said.

"I do have two more thoughts," Kristy went on.

She was speaking hesitantly, and I noticed Claudia glance at her sharply.

"Number four is lower rates." (This caused another groan from Claudia.) "*Just enough* lower," said Kristy defensively, "to

331

undercut the Baby-sitters Agency."

"But we don't know what they earn," I protested.

"We will soon," said Kristy. "I'll find out. And number five is . . . is to do what the agency does—take on late jobs or jobs we can't handle by giving them to older kids. Sam and Charlie baby-sit sometimes, and Janine cou—"

"NO!" cried Claudia. "No. Kristy, this is getting out of hand. The Kid-Kit is a good idea, but lower rates and housework and giving away our jobs? No, no, no. If that's what this club is going to become, then I don't want to be in it."

"Me neither," said Mary Anne softly.

Not be in the club? If both of them left, there wouldn't *be* any more club. They didn't mean it. They didn't *really* mean it. What would I do without the club? Talking to Pete on the phone was nice, and sitting with the group in the cafeteria was fun, but those kids weren't true friends like Claudia and Kristy and Mary Anne.

I needed the club.

"You guys," I said, "I don't want the Babysitters Club to fall apart. We can't let Liz and Michelle beat us. We have to prove that we can succeed, too."

"Yes," agreed Claudia, "But not the way Kristy said. That's—that's—what's the word?"

"Degrading?" suggested Mary Anne.

"Yes. That's it. Degrading."

"Well, what do *you* think we should do," snapped Kristy, "since you know so much?"

"I think," said Claudia, "That we should use two of your ideas—the Kid-Kit and the special deals—and save the other things, especially number five, as last resorts."

"That sounds like a good plan," said Mary Anne. "Anyway, we wouldn't want to use up all your ideas at once."

"That's true," I said.

"All right," said Kristy, with a sigh. She sent me a troubled look. I shrugged. Kristy knew I was on her side, but we both realized that we shouldn't overdo things.

"Come on," said Claudia. "Let's start making the Kid-Kit boxes now. It'll be fun! You guys each get a box from home, and come back here. I have crayons and fabric and paints and all sorts of things we can decorate them with." (Claudia loves art.)

"We'll make the best boxes ever!" I said, trying to sound enthusiastic. "In fact, we'll be the best baby-sitters ever! Let's get to work!"

4th CHAPTER

The following Monday was a glorious, warm day that felt more like May than the middle of November. At exactly three-thirty, armed with my Kid-Kit, I rang the bell at Charlotte Johanssen's house. Charlotte, who's seven, is one of my favourite baby-sitting kids. Her mother is a doctor and her father is an engineer. Charlotte is an only child who's very smart, but is shy and doesn't have many friends. I can sympathize when she gets lonely.

Dr Johanssen answered the door. "Hello, Stacey," she said cheerfully, even though she looked quite tired. That Monday must have been one of her days off, because Dr Johanssen is usually working at Stoney-brook Medical Centre. Her schedule changes from month to month.

"Hi!" I replied.

"How have you been feeling?" Dr

334

Johanssen always asks me that. When anyone else asks, I get annoyed, but not with Charlotte's mother.

"Hungry," I said honestly. "And I've lost some weight."

"Any problems with your insulin or your blood sugar level?"

"Nope. I think I just need to eat more. After all, I am twelve."

"That sounds sensible. What are you doing about the problem, though?"

"Mum called Dr Frank today, but she hasn't been able to talk to him yet. I guess she'll know something by the time I get home."

"Stacey! Hi, Stacey!" Charlotte bounced into the hallway, beaming. She's always glad to see me.

"Hi, there," I said.

"What's that box?"

"Something special. I'll open it as soon as your mum leaves."

"Mum, go, go!" cried Charlotte. She never wants her parents to leave, even when I'm the baby-sitter.

"Is that a hint?" asked Dr Johanssen, pulling on a sweater.

"I think so," I said.

"All right, girls. This meeting will be a quickie, I hope. I should be home between five and five-thirty."

"See you later, Mum." Charlotte practically pushed her mother out the door.

"Now?" she asked me.

"Just let me take my jacket off." I hung it in the front hall cupboard, while Charlotte hopped impatiently from one foot to the other. Then we sat down on the floor in the living room.

"Can you read what this says?" I asked, pointing to the words on the lid.

Charlotte leaned over for a better look. "Kid-Kit," she said promptly. "It's pretty." I had covered my box with blue flowered fabric and glued white rickrack along the borders. Then I had cut the letters for "Kid-Kit" from green felt.

"Thanks. I'll bring this with me every time I baby-sit." I lifted the lid. "There's all sorts of fun stuff in here. And I'll change it once a month."

"Oh, great," said Charlotte softly as she pulled the things out of the box. "Snakes and Ladders . . . Spill and Spell . . . *The Cricket in Times Square*. What's this book about?"

"Oh, you'll love it, I think. It's about a cricket named Chester who accidentally winds up in the middle of New York City, and makes friends with a mouse named Tucker, a cat named Harry, and a boy named Mario. We can read a little each time I baby-sit. And I can tell you about New York." Charlotte loves to hear about when I lived in the city. "And after we finish that book, we can read *Tucker's Countryside* and

Harry Cat's Pet Puppy, which are more stories about those animals."

"Goody." Charlotte continued to look through the crayons and chalk and drawing paper, the jigsaw puzzle and jacks.

"We can do anything you want," I said, "but even though I brought the Kid-Kit, I have one other idea."

"What?"

"We could walk downtown. It's such a beautiful day. We could look in the store windows and find out what's playing at the cinema, and maybe stop off at your school playground on the way home."

Charlotte looked as if someone were holding out two huge ice-cream cones, each made from one of her favourite flavours, and telling her she could have only one of them. She glanced out of the window at the sunshine, pawed through the box once more, and then looked at me. "Downtown," she said at last, "if you promise to bring the Kid-Kit back."

I crossed my heart. "Promise."

So we put our jackets on and walked towards town. The centre of Stoneybrook is about a kilometre from Charlotte's house. We could run there in ten minutes or walk there (fast) in under twenty, but we dawdled along, taking our time. Charlotte kept stopping to pick up acorns.

"I should save these," she said. "Then if

I ever got a pet squirrel, I could feed them to him."

"Now what would you do with a pet squirrel?" I asked her.

"Talk to him."

"But you have Carrot. You can talk to him." (Carrot is the Johanssens' schnauzer.)

"It would be nice to have more than one person to talk to."

"Don't you have any friends, Charlotte? I mean, people-friends?"

Charlotte shook her head. She stooped down, picked up a particularly fat acorn, and stuffed it in her pocket as she stood up.

I looked at Charlotte. She's pretty—chestnut brown hair, big, dark eyes, and dimples in her cheeks when she smiles. She's smart, she's considerate, and she's sweet. So what was wrong with her? Why didn't she have any friends?

"The kids don't like me," she said, "and I don't like them."

"The kids in your class?" I asked. "Why don't you like them?"

"Because they don't like me."

"All right, why don't they like you?"

Charlotte shrugged. Then she stuck one thumb in her mouth and put her other hand in mine. We walked in silence until we reached the town.

"What shall we do?" I asked.

Charlotte perked up. She took her thumb out of her mouth. "The sweet shop!"

"Okay." Polly's Store is pretty spectacular as candy stores go. It's even better than a lot of sweet shops in New York. I could understand why Charlotte wanted to go to it. It's a sort of fairyland. And in November, with the holidays just around the corner, it was more spectacular than usual.

The only thing I don't like about Polly's Store is Polly. She runs the shop and is about a hundred years old. Her younger sister, who looks every bit as old as Polly, helps her. Any time kids go in the shop, they fasten their eyeballs on them, and don't take them off until the kids leave. But Charlotte and I were prepared to brave the sisters.

We approached the store. Long before we reached the doorway, we could smell chocolate. We breathed it in.

"Mmm, heavenly," I said.

"Yeah, heavenly," echoed Charlotte.

We looked in the windows. One was ready for Thanksgiving. The biggest chocolate turkey I'd ever seen was surrounded by smaller chocolate turkeys. They were standing in a bed of sweet popcorn and gumdrops.

Charlotte and I looked at each other and smiled.

"Now the other window," said Charlotte.

We crossed in front of the doorway and gazed at the second window.

"Christmas already?" asked Charlotte, staring at a tree and Santa and presents. She looked both perplexed and dreamy. "Stacey, how long? How many days?"

"Pretty long, Char. About five weeks. The stores like to get ready early. Come on, let's go inside."

We walked through the doorway, and I was pleased to see that we weren't the only people in the little shop. Three other customers were there, and Polly and her sister were busy helping them—which meant that they were too busy to watch Charlotte and me.

The outside of Polly's Store had smelled of chocolate. The inside smelled of chocolate, and much more—ginger and cinnamon and liquorice and marzipan and cream and raspberry filling and roasted nuts and raisins and cherries and spun sugar. The air was heady and warm. It was almost more than I could stand. I tried to figure out how much it would hurt to have just one piece of white chocolate.

"Look, Stacey!" Charlotte cried. She ran to a display of elaborate gingerbread houses decorated with smarties and white frosting. "Oh, elves! And mice. Look at all the little creatures that live in those houses. . . . Oh!" She grabbed my hand and pulled me to the penny candy counter. We were facing bin after bin of sweets: butterscotch drops and chocolates and toffees and liquorice sticks and peppermints. . . .

"Please, Stacey, could we get just one

thing? *One* thing each?" pleaded Charlotte.

I noticed bite-sized bars of white chocolate and thought I could actually *taste* one melting in my mouth.

I felt in my pocket. I had two quarters, more than enough for two pieces of chocolate.

"*Please?*"

I pulled the money out and put it on the counter. At that moment, Polly's cuckoo clock chimed. It was four-thirty. Slowly, I put the money back in my pocket, and let out my breath. I couldn't believe what I'd almost done.

"Better not," I said. "It's too close to dinner. Your mum doesn't like you eating sweets, anyway."

"I know," said Charlotte. "I just thought—"

"It's okay. I wanted a treat, too, but you're not the only one who's not supposed to eat sweets. Come on, let's go."

We left the store, Charlotte looking longingly over her shoulder.

"Hey!" I said. "We have enough time to go to the playground before we head home."

"Goody!"

It was growing dark, but I thought we could play safely for ten minutes. I felt better when we reached the school and saw a group of children hanging from the monkey bars. "Come on," I said. But Charlotte had stopped in her tracks.

341

"No."

"It's okay. It's not dark yet. And there are other kids here."

"No. I want to go home. Let's go."

Too late. The children had spotted Charlotte.

"Hey, there's *Char*-Char," cried one.

"Hey, teacher's pet! Go away!"

"Yeah! Charlotte, Charlotte, go away, don't come back another day!"

"Teacher's pet, teacher's pet. . . ."

"*I am not the teacher's pet!*" shouted Charlotte. She turned and began running home.

"Hey! Wait! Charlotte?" I caught up with her easily.

"Go away."

"It's me, Stacey."

"I said go away."

"I can't. I'm your baby-sitter. I have to stay with you."

Charlotte marched straight ahead, chin held high, tears dripping down her cheeks.

"Did those kids tease you because they saw you with a baby-sitter? . . . Charlotte?" I tagged along at her side.

"No," she said at last, sniffling. "They don't know you're my sitter."

"Why are you mad at me?"

Charlotte stopped walking. "I'm not mad at you."

"Just upset because they teased you?"

"I guess."

"How come they teased you?"

"I don't know."

"They called you the teacher's pet."

"I don't want to talk about it."

"Hey, listen, I got teased a *lot* last year."

"In New York?"

"In New York."

"Who teased you?"

"My best friend. Well, she used to be my best friend. Now she's my former best friend."

"Why did she tease you?"

"It's a long story."

"Don't you want to talk about it, either?"

"I guess not."

We were approaching the corner of Charlotte's street. She had stopped crying and was holding my hand again. Suddenly she squealed and pointed to something. "Look at that!"

I looked. All I could see in the dusky light was a bunch of helium balloons bobbing down the street towards us. I looked harder and realized that a person was behind them. Either that, or the balloons were propelled by a pair of legs wearing jeans and sneakers.

"The balloons spoke. "Hi!"

I peered around them. Holding tightly to a handful of strings was a pretty girl, probably a couple of years older than I, tall and very thin, wearing a sweat shirt I would have died for.

She separated a red balloon from the

bunch and handed it to Charlotte. Then she turned to me. "I'm Liz Lewis," she said, "chairman of the Baby-sitters Agency. I hope you'll call me if you ever need a sitter for your little sister." Charlotte giggled. "The number's on the balloon. See you!" She walked on.

A shiver ran down my spine, and I suddenly felt cold through and through.

Charlotte was holding the balloon in both hands. She turned it around and read slowly, "The Baby-sitters Agency. Call Liz Lewis 51162 or Michelle Patterson 57548." She looked up at me. "More baby-sitters? What's an agency, Stacey?"

"It's another long story. Come on. Let's go home."

I knew I'd be on the phone with Kristy again that evening.

5th CHAPTER

Sunday, November 23

It is almost one week since Liz Lewis and Michelle Patterson sent around their fliers. Usually, our club gets about fourteen or fifteen jobs a week. Since last Monday, we've had nine. That's why I'm writing in our notebook. This book is supposed to be a diary of our baby-sitting jobs, so each of us can write up our problems and experiences for the other club members to read. But the Baby-sitters Agency is the biggest problem we've ever had, and I plan to keep track of it in our notebook. We better do something fast.

Kristy was worried. She took the balloons as a personal insult. It turned out that she'd run into Liz that afternoon herself. Only Kristy had had the nerve to tell Liz who she was—chairman of the Babysitters *Club*, and therefore Liz's number one rival. According to Kristy, they had "exchanged words," which I guess meant that they had had an argument. But by the time I was talking to Kristy over the phone in the evening, all she could say was, "Why didn't *we* think of balloons? Why didn't *we* think of balloons?"

The very next day, though, Monday, something wonderful happened that took our minds off the agency—followed by something horrible that put our minds right back on it.

The Babysitters Club had walked home from school together. When we reached Bradford Court, Claudia went to her house to work on a painting for art class, and Mary Anne went to her house because she was supposed to bake cranberry bread for the Thanksgiving dinner she and her father would be sharing with Kristy's family (which included Watson, Kristy's step-father-to-be, and his two little kids; Kristy said it was going to be one interesting meal).

"Want to come over for a while?" Kristy asked me after Claudia and Mary Anne had left. (Not one of us had a baby-sitting job that afternoon.)

"Sure," I replied, eager for even a *look* at Sam Thomas.

We stepped up to her front door and Kristy took her house key out of her purse. Since her parents are divorced and Mrs Thomas works full-time, Kristy is often the first person home in the afternoon. But when she put the key in the lock, she discovered that the door was open.

"That's odd," she murmured. "I hope David Michael didn't get here first. He hates to come home to an empty house." We walked into the front hall. Kristy's mother was there.

"Mum! What are you doing home?" exclaimed Kristy.

Mrs Thomas smiled. "Hi, honey. Hi, Stacey."

"Hi, Mrs Thomas," I replied.

"Look who's here with me," said Kristy's mother.

"Who?" asked Kristy suspiciously.

"Come in the kitchen."

Sitting at the kitchen table was Jamie Newton. He was drinking milk and colouring in a colouring book.

"Jamie!" cried Kristy. "Hi!"

"Hi there, Jamie," I said.

"Hi-hi," answered Jamie cheerfully.

"What are you doing here?" Kristy asked him.

Jamie glanced at Kristy's mother.

"Go ahead and tell them your news, sweetie," said Mrs Thomas.

"My mummy's having a baby," he

announced. "She's at the hospital."

"Having the baby? *Now?*" asked Kristy, sounding dismayed.

"Kristy, I know you girls had plans for helping the Newtons out," her mother said, "but the baby started to come late this morning. Several weeks ago, the Newtons had asked me whether I'd be able to watch Jamie if the baby arrived at night or while you girls were in school. I told them I'd be glad to. When Mr Newton called me at work to say that it was time for him to take his wife to the hospital, I told him just to drop Jamie at my office on the way."

"On the way!" said Kristy. "But you work in Stamford."

"I know. The Newtons' doctor is with the Stamford hospital, though, so I really was on their way. Jamie worked very hard with me today, didn't you, Jamie?"

Jamie nodded proudly.

"He made a picture for the baby and read some books and copied things on the xerox machine."

"And we had lunch together," added Jamie.

"That's right," said Mrs Thomas. "We ate in the cafeteria." She looked at her watch. "And now, girls," she said. "I'm leaving Jamie in your capable hands and going back to the office for a few hours."

I got the distinct impression that Mrs

Thomas hadn't got much work done that day.

"But Mum, wait! What about the baby?" asked Kristy. "Don't leave us hanging!"

"Yeah!" I exclaimed. "What did Mrs Newton have?"

"Sorry, no word yet. Mr Newton promised he'd phone as soon as the baby is born. He knows to call here after three o'clock."

"Well, how long does it take?" asked Kristy indignantly. "I mean, to have a baby?"

Her mother smiled. "It depends on the baby. You took twenty-four hours."

"Wow," I said.

"*Twenty-four hours!*" cried Kristy. "Oh, no. I can*not* wait that long."

"Well, maybe this baby will come faster. Now listen. Jamie's going to stay with us until his father comes home from the hospital. Since he may be spending the night, why don't you get his pyjamas and things, but stay around here the rest of the time. It'll be easier for Jamie than going back and forth. Here's the key to the Newtons' house. I'll pay you for sitting this afternoon, by the way. And I'll be home by six-thirty." Mrs Thomas kissed Kristy goodbye and waved to Jamie and me. Then she was gone.

"Well, this isn't exactly the way I'd thought things would work out," said

Kristy, "but it *is* a pretty exciting afternoon."

"I'll say! . . . Hey, where are your brothers?"

"You mean Sam?" teased Kristy.

"We-ell. . . ."

"Let's see. Today's Monday so it's Charlie's day to watch David Michael. Oh, I bet he met David Michael at school and took him back to Stoneybrook High to watch cheerleader practice. Sam's probably with them."

"Cheerleader practice?"

"Yeah. David Michael loves it. He comes home and shows us the cheers."

I giggled.

"So, Jamie," said Kristy. "What do you think? You're going to be a brother pretty soon."

Jamie shrugged and continued colouring.

"What do you want?" I asked him. "A brother or a sister?"

"Brother."

"Aren't you excited?"

Jamie shrugged again.

Kristy and I glanced at each other.

"You know," I said suddenly, not at all sure where the idea came from, "being a big brother is so important that I think you ought to have a Big Brother Party, Jamie."

Jamie looked at me with wide eyes.

Kristy jumped in immediately, understanding just what I meant. "That's right," she said. "We should celebrate this afternoon. We'll have a special Big Brother Party for our favourite big brother—you."

"A party for *me*?" said Jamie, his voice squeaking.

"Yeah, we'll invite everyone," I added. "Kristy, do you think your mother will mind?"

"No."

I dashed to the phone and began dialling. In ten minutes I had spread the news to Claudia, Mary Anne, Charlotte, and the Pike kids. I'd also called a few other baby-sitting charges but they weren't home.

"Well," I said to Kristy and Jamie when I was finished, "Claudia's on her way over, Mary Anne will come when she finishes the batter for the cranberry bread—she says she can bake it tonight—Charlotte's coming, and Mallory Pike is going to bring Claire and Margo over." (There are eight Pike kids. Mallory's ten, and Claire and Margo are four and six.)

"Terrific!" cried Kristy. She was rummaging around in the kitchen and had pulled out a bag of marshmallows, several apples, a can of juice, and a carrot which I assumed was for me. "Claudia's bringing over something from her room," she added. "Pretzels, I think. Jamie, what would you like to do at your party? Play games?" She began to slice the apples.

Jamie nodded.

"What games?" I asked.

Jamie looked blank.

"Put a record on the stereo in the playroom and spread a bath mat on the floor," Kristy instructed me. "We can play musical rug. It's easier than musical chairs. I'll explain later."

"All right," I replied. "And we can have egg races, you know, with spoons. And the kids can make paper masks. We'll have a contest for the funniest one."

"Good idea. Then when it's time to calm everyone down, we'll see if we can get Mary Anne to read *The Little Engine That Could*. She makes it really funny, using all these different voices."

"Oh, boy!" exclaimed Jamie. "Oh, boy!"

At that moment, Claudia arrived. Charlotte was right behind her. I gave her a hug. The Pikes showed up next, and just after Mary Anne arrived, Charlie walked in with David Michael. I was so excited about the Big Brother Party that I was only a little disappointed that Sam wasn't there.

The little kids—Jamie, David Michael, Claire, and Margo—gathered excitedly in the playroom which I had decorated hastily with a roll of green crepe paper. The members of the Babysitters Club looked on proudly. Mallory wandered between the two groups. But Charlotte hung back.

"Everything okay?" I asked her. She nodded shyly. "Why don't you come over here with me." I led her to the group of kids. "This is Jamie. You know Jamie Newton, right?" Charlotte nodded again. "He's our guest of honour. He's going to become a big brother."

Jamie beamed.

"Make way for the food!" called Kristy, carrying a tray of food in from the kitchen. Charlie followed her, bringing napkins, plates, and paper cups. Then he left. I don't think Big Brother Parties held any interest for him.

"Eat now, games later!" Kristy announced. She turned to Mary Anne and Claudia and me. "Take the food away in twenty minutes no matter what," she whispered. "Otherwise they're going to spoil their appetites for dinner."

Everybody helped themselves to the food. Claudia gave Jamie a paper crown to wear while he ate. When twenty minutes were up, we returned the food to the kitchen. Then the games began. Charlotte wouldn't join in musical rug or the egg races, but she did enter the mask contest. Claudia had just finished awarding prizes for the masks (we had decided that each of the kids should win a prize) when the phone rang.

"Kristy!" Charlie called from the kitchen. "Phone! It's Mr Newton!"

"Aughh!" shrieked Kristy.

"Jamie, it's Daddy!" I cried. "Come on!"

The entire party ran into the kitchen.

Charlie made a fast getaway.

Kristy grabbed up the phone. "Hello? Mr Newton? . . . She did? . . . She *did*? Oh, that's *great*! It's super! . . . How much? . . . Wow. . . . Yeah, sure. Here he is." Kristy handed the phone to Jamie. "Your daddy wants to talk to you."

Jamie took the receiver and held it to his ear.

"Say hello," prompted Kristy.

"Hello. Daddy? . . . Fine. We're having a party. . . . Okay. . . . Okay. . . . Okay. . . . 'Bye."

Kristy took the phone back. "When do you think you'll be home?" she asked Mr Newton. "Oh, okay. Well, we'll give Jamie dinner. You can pick him up any time. . . . You're welcome. And congratulations! 'Bye."

Kristy hung up the phone and faced us.

"What is it? What is it? What *is* it?" I cried.

"It's a—"

"Girl," supplied Jamie quietly.

We all began shrieking.

"She weighs nine pounds," added Kristy, "and her name is Lucy Jane."

More shrieking.

In the midst of the noise and excitement, I realized that Jamie was gone. I dashed out of the kitchen and checked the bathroom. No Jamie. Frantically, I ran through the first floor of the Thomases' house. I found him in the laundry room sitting next to Louie, crying.

I stepped in and sat beside him on the floor. "What's wrong, Big Brother?" I asked.

"The baby's here."

"And you wanted a boy instead of a girl, right?"

Jamie shrugged.

"Don't you like her name? I think Lucy is a pretty name."

"It's okay."

"It's a big change, huh?"

Jamie nodded.

"Your family will be different."

"Yup," said Jamie. "And that's not all."

"What do you mean?"

"Something else will be different. There will be lots of changes."

"What else will be different?" I asked.

"Kristy can't baby-sit me any more."

"What do you mean?" That cold feeling crept into my stomach again.

"Mummy called a girl and said, 'We need an older sitter for the new baby.' "

"Was the girl named Liz Lewis?" I whispered.

"I think so. But . . . but. . . ." Jamie's tears started to fall again, "I want *Kristy*!"

I pulled Jamie into my lap and sat with him for a while. Louie leaned against me and looked at us with mournful eyes.

I tried to be calm and rational. Jamie was

just three years old. He had only overheard one end of a phone conversation. He wasn't even sure that Liz Lewis was the name he had overheard. Furthermore, just because Mrs Newton had talked to someone about finding older sitters didn't mean she wasn't going to use the Babysitters Club any more.

So why did I feel as if an icicle were sitting in my stomach?

I knew why. It was because it made sense that Mrs Newton would want someone older to take care of a newborn baby. And Liz Lewis and Michelle Patterson could provide that for her.

The Babysitters Club couldn't.

Still, I felt that Mrs Newton was being a traitor. After all, Kristy was Jamie's favourite baby-sitter, and the rest of the members of our club were the Newtons' other regular sitters. We could handle caring for an infant. We were very responsible. And I was willing to bet that Liz and Michelle's sitters, even if they were in high school, weren't responsible at all. The more I thought about the Baby-sitters Agency, the angrier I felt.

Later, when the Big Brother Party was breaking up, I told Kristy what Jamie had overheard. She looked aghast. "And you know what?" I said suddenly, the anger building up inside me again.

Kristy shook her head.

"This"—I narrowed my eyes and set my jaw—"means war."

6th CHAPTER

I was all set to launch a war against the Baby-sitters Agency. So was Kristy. We were ready to let loose with every single plan or idea she had come up with. But Claudia put her foot down (so did Mary Anne), and while we were wasting time trying to decide what to do, the Baby-sitters Agency got one more step ahead of us.

The club hadn't even had a chance for a proper meeting to discuss Jamie's bad news, since Monday's meeting had been held hastily after the Big Brother Party, and Kristy and Mary Anne weren't present because they were at the Thomases' watching Jamie and cleaning up. Then on Tuesday, the very next day, the Baby-sitters Agency carried out another step in their scheme to take away our club's business. (I don't know if that's how *they* thought of what they were doing, but it's how *I* thought of it. At any rate, they were big copycats in the first place, for starting a club so much like ours and giving it a name so close to ours.)

But I'm getting off the track. On Tuesday morning, the Babysitters Club walked to school as a group, which was nice, because in the beginning, the club kept separating into two and two—Kristy and Mary Anne, Claudia and me. But that started to change when Kristy became a *little* interested in boys, and I wanted to have more than one close friend. Anyway, we arrived at school and guess what was there to meet us? The Baby-sitters Agency. Everywhere. Michelle and Liz were trying to recruit more sitters to call on when job requests came in.

Liz was standing on the front steps of the school handing out her agency balloons along with fliers. Mary Anne managed to get a flier—not from Liz but from a boy who was about to toss his in a dustbin. It was a different flier from the one Claudia's sister had brought to us.

"Look at this," said Mary Anne. She read aloud from the flier. " 'Want to earn fast money the easy way?' "

"Fast money!" cried Kristy indignantly. "The *easy* way! Liz must be crazy. Really. That girl is off her rocker."

"Wait, wait. Let's hear this," I said. "Go on, Mary Anne."

We were standing in a tense bunch,

huddled together a few yards away from Liz. I could feel Liz's triumphant eyes on us, but I didn't give her the satisfaction of turning around.

" 'Join the Baby-sitters Agency,' " Mary Anne continued. " 'You do the work, but we do the hardest part of the job. Let the agency find jobs *for* you!' "

The flier went on to explain how the agency worked, which was just about the way Kristy had guessed when she'd made her fake phone call, looking for a sitter for "Harry Kane." We had to admit that the fliers made the agency look pretty tempting. All you had to do was join—then sit back and wait for Liz or Michelle to hand you a job. Of course, you didn't get to keep all the money you earned. You had to turn some of it over to the agency (that was how Liz and Michelle made money when *they* weren't sitting), but we thought that a lot of kids would find that a small price to pay for the extra jobs they'd get through the agency.

"Boy," said Mary Anne. She scrunched up the flier and threw it in the bin. "The agency is probably going to have a million eighth-graders working for it."

"Yeah," said Claudia glumly, kicking a pebble with the toe of her sneaker. "For all we know, Liz and Michelle have someone recruiting sitters over at the high school, too. They could be getting twelfth-graders. I bet a senior in high school could stay out until two in the morning—or even spend the night."

"Or sit for a whole darned weekend," I said.

"But how does the agency know what kind of sitter they're giving their clients?" asked Mary Anne. "They could give someone a really irresponsible kid who just wants to make a few bucks."

"Right," said Kristy, "but why should Liz and Michelle care, as long as they get their cut of the money earned?"

We walked dejectedly into the building, carefully not looking at Liz as we went by her. I remembered something my father had said to me the year before. He'd said it when I was in the hospital after one of the times I'd gone into insulin shock in school—in the cafeteria, where absolutely *every*one had seen me fall forward into a bowl of tomato soup—and had been taken away in the ambulance. "Stacey, look at it this way, honey. The worst has happened," he'd told me. "Now things can only get better." It was a good philosophy, and I'd repeated it to myself many times since then.

"Well, you guys," I said to the members of the Babysitters Club as we entered the school building, "Look at it this way. The worst has happened. Now things can only get better."

"Wrong," said Kristy flatly.

"What?"

"She said 'wrong,' " Claudia repeated. "Look."

We were rounding a corner. I glanced up. In the main intersection of Stoneybrook Middle School a counter had been set up. A large sign on the wall behind it screamed: THE BABY-SITTERS AGENCY, and in smaller letters: SIGN UP HERE.

Michelle Patterson and two eighth-grade girls were sitting behind the counter. Each was holding a clipboard and looked very official. A large group of girls from every grade, as well as three boys, were standing around the counter asking questions and talking to Michelle and her helpers. I couldn't tell how many of them were signing up, but it didn't matter.

"I wonder who gave them permission to do *that*," I said.

Claudia shrugged.

"Toilets," said Kristy urgently. We left the hall and piled into the nearest girls' toilet, checking to make sure the cubicles were empty. Then Kristy, glaring furiously at Claudia and Mary Anne, opened her mouth to speak.

Claudia beat her to it. "Don't say it. I know what you're going to say. Okay. So we were wrong and you were right. What do you want to do about the agency? We'll do anything."

"Anything?" asked Kristy. She looked at each of us in turn.

"Anything," said Claudia.

"Ditto," said Mary Anne.

"Double ditto," I said.

"Great," said Kristy, "because I have another idea. A new one."

"Y-you do?" asked Claudia.

Kristy nodded grimly.

Claudia glanced sideways at Mary Anne. She poked at a drop of water on a tap. "What? I'm afraid to ask."

At that moment, the bell rang.

Kristy rolled her eyes. "No time now. I don't care what *any* of you is doing after school. I'm calling a triple-emergency club meeting."

"Why not at break today?" asked Mary Anne.

"Too risky," replied Kristy. "No more club business at school. For all we know, the agency has spies watching us. Anyone sitting this afternoon?"

We shook our heads.

"I haven't even spoken to Dr or Mr Johanssen in a week," I murmured.

"I thought as much," said Kristy. "Well, today's my regular afternoon with David Michael, so we'll have to hold the meeting at my house, okay?"

"Okay," we agreed.

The meeting that afternoon was the picture of depression. The Babysitters Club sat around Kristy's dining room table while David Michael built a house out of wooden blocks for Louie. Kristy had served herself and Claudia and Mary Anne a snack, and had poured each of us a diet soda, but the food remained untouched. We stared at our hands. Claudia shredded a paper napkin and arranged the strips in a tidy pile. Nobody spoke except Kristy.

"We can talk about my other ideas later," she said, "but the new one is to recruit more members—eighth-graders—for our club. That way we'll have some older sitters, but we won't have to copy the agency by working the way they do." She looked around the table? "Agreed?"

Claudia, Mary Anne, and I nodded silently.

The Babysitters Club was going to increase its numbers.

7th CHAPTER

Thanksgiving vacation was not a lot of fun that year. It came just two days after the Babysitters Club decided to take on new members. I didn't really mind asking other people to join our club—I figured it would be a chance to make more friends—but I didn't like the *reason* we were adding members. I was hopping mad at Liz and Michelle for hurting our club.

That was pretty much all I could think about on Thursday and Friday of Thanksgiving vacation. We had a four-day weekend, and I spent the first half of it mad at the Baby-sitters Agency.

I spent the second half of it mad at my parents.

For starters, they had said way back over the summer that we could go to New York for Thanksgiving, but the weekend before Thanksgiving they had suddenly

364

changed their minds.

"We thought it would be nice to make our first Thanksgiving in Connecticut a true old fashioned, New England holiday," Mum said. I'll cook a meal that you can eat"—I scowled—"and we'll spend the day by ourselves. Dad will build a fire in the fireplace. We'll just enjoy being cosy and together in our new home."

That didn't sound so bad. In fact, I managed to enjoy our day. It even snowed a little. It was late the next day, when Mum and Dad told me the real reason for not going to New York, that I got angry at them.

They had taken me to Washington Mall which is about half an hour away from Stoneybrook. For some reason, the day after Thanksgiving is the biggest Christmas shopping day of the season. I don't know why. But I love to shop, so I thought the excursion would be fun, and would help take my mind off the Baby-sitters Agency. Kristy had told me all about Washington Mall. It's the biggest one around, with five levels of stores, a zillion restaurants and food stands, four cinemas, a video game arcade, a pet zoo, and an exhibits area.

I had taken some of the money I'd earned baby-sitting out of my savings account, and I left Mum and Dad to explore the mall on my own. I bought two Christmas presents —a pair of striped leg warmers for Claudia, and a book about New York for Mary Anne—and a dinosaur pin for me. I planned to attach it to my beret.

At one o'clock I met Mum and Dad and we ate lunch in a sandwich shop. After lunch we went to a movie. Two hours later, as we filed back into the mall, Dad said brightly, "Well, how about one more treat before we head home? We could go to that little French cafe on the top level."

"Ooh, goody," I said.

When we were settled, Dad with a cup of coffee, Mum with a glass of wine, and I with diet ginger ale, Dad glanced at Mum, and said, "Now, honey?"

"What?" I asked, immediately suspicious.

"We have some news for you."

"What is it?"

Mum and Dad kept looking at each other as if they couldn't decide who should tell me the news. I knew it must be pretty important. Furthermore, I had a feeling that whatever it was, I wasn't going to like it one bit.

"We aren't moving again, are we?" I asked.

"Heavens, no," said Mum. "It's not bad news . . . exactly."

"You're pregnant!" I cried. "You found out you can have a baby after all!"

"*Shh!*" said Dad. "People are turning around."

"Well, *what*?"

Mum cleared her throat. "It's just that we've scheduled the tests with the new doctor I mentioned to you a couple of weeks ago, remember?"

"How could I forget?"

"Stacey," said Dad warningly, his voice rising on the last syllable.

"Sorry."

"They're going to be a little later in the month than we had thought."

"Near *Christ*mas?" I asked, dismayed.

"We'll leave on Friday, the twelfth, and probably return on Wednesday, the seventeenth."

"But—but that's five days!" I sputtered. "You said it would only be three days."

"Well, you'll still miss just three days of school," said my father. "When we found out the tests would take longer than we realized, we scheduled them over a weekend. That's why we didn't go to New York for Thanksgiving. Two long weekends there so close together are too many."

"Am I going to be in the *hospital* for five days?" Being in the hospital when you feel fine has to be the most boring thing in the world.

"You'll spend a lot of time at this doctor's clinic," replied Mum, "but you'll be an outpatient.... Look, in the evenings we can have fun. And we'll have Sunday free. We can visit your cousins and go Christmas shopping—"

"*And*," said Dad, grinning, "I got tickets to the Sunday performance of *Paris Magic*."

"*Paris Magic!*" I cried, momentarily forgetting doctors and clinics. "You're kidding! I can't believe it! Oh, thank you!" *Paris Magic* was a musical I'd been dying to see.

"And we'll go to Rockefeller Center and look at the Christmas tree," Mum went on. "Think of it, Stacey. Christmas in New York. You always liked the city best at that season."

"I guess," I replied, returning to earth. Tickets to *Paris Magic* didn't make up for what Mum and Dad were doing to me. "So what does Dr Werner think of . . . what's the name of the new doctor?"

"Dr Barnes," said Dad.

"What does Dr Werner think of Dr Barnes?"

"She doesn't know about Dr Barnes yet," replied my mother.

"Mu-um. I'd like to check with Dr Werner first."

"Stacey," said Dad. "You are not in charge here. Your mother and I make the decisions."

"Decisions about *me*, *my* body."

"That's what parents are for," he said wryly.

"So what's so special about Dr Barnes?" I asked. "Why do we have to see him . . . or her?"

368

"Him," said Mum. "He's a holistic doctor."

Holistic. . . holy? "A *faith* healer?" I squeaked." You're taking me to a religious person for a miracle?" Mum and Dad had considered some pretty desperate things over the months, but nothing like faith healing.

"Stacey, for pity's sake. *No*," said Dad. "Calm down. Holistic medicine deals with the whole body, with a person as a whole, made up not just of physical parts, but of mental, emotional, environmental, nutritional—"

"I get it, I get it," I muttered, embarrassed.

Dad drained his coffee, Mum sipped her wine, and I stirred my soda with the straw.

"Well," said Dad at last, "we just wanted you to know what to expect. And to keep those days open for our trip."

"What about my school work?" I asked.

"We'll talk to your teachers before we leave. Maybe you can bring some of your homework with you and do it at the clinic," said Mum. "Then you won't be too far behind when you return."

I nodded. "I think this is very unfair," I said softly.

My parents sighed in unison. "Well, we're sorry, honey," replied Mum. "But this is the way things are."

On Saturday afternoon, I baby-sat for Charlotte Johanssen. It was my first job in over a week. I knew that her parents were using the agency in the evenings because then they didn't have to worry about being home early. I hadn't seen Charlotte since the Big Brother Party. I brought the Kid-Kit with me as I had promised, and we began reading *The Cricket in Times Square*.

When the Johanssens came home, I waited until Dr Johanssen had paid me before I finally asked, "Could I talk to you? Please?"

"Of course, Stacey," Charlotte's mother replied. "Let's go in the den."

We walked across the hall and Dr Johanssen closed the door behind us. "What's up? Are you feeling all right?" she asked.

"That's just the trouble. I'm fine. But Mum and Dad want me to see another new doctor in New York. He's going to do all these tests at his clinic. We have to go away for *five days*."

Dr Johanssen shook her head in sympathy.

"He's a holistic doctor. Dad explained what that means." I giggled. "I thought it meant he was holy—a faith healer."

Charlotte's mother didn't smile, though. She looked at me sharply. "Holistic. A clinic? Do you know the doctor's name?"

"Dr Barnes."

Dr Johanssen groaned. "You weren't too far wrong, Stacey. Dr Barnes *calls* himself a holistic doctor but he practically *is* a faith healer. At any rate, I don't think he's much more than a quack. He just happens to be getting a lot of publicity now. He's a fad doctor. And he's giving good holistic doctors a bad reputation. I don't know him personally," she added, "I've just heard about him."

"I knew it, I knew it," I moaned.

"Now don't worry. Dr Barnes isn't going to harm you, from what I've heard. He won't touch your insulin, and if he changes your diet, it will be only slightly. What he is going to do—I can practically guarantee this—is recommend all sorts of expensive programmes and therapies designed to make your life as positive and fulfilling and healthy as possible. He'll tell your parents that this will enable you to rid your body of the disease."

"What kinds of therapies?" I asked.

"Oh, everything. He'll tell your parents to send you to a psychologist or psychiatrist. He'll give you an exercise programme, start you on recreational therapy. He may even recommend that you change schools so you can get individualized instruction."

"No!" I cried.

"There's nothing really wrong with any of those things. It's just that—well, it's my belief that no special programme is going to rid your body of diabetes."

I stood up. "Of course not! Are they crazy? How is a psychiatrist going to change my blood sugar? Dr Johanssen, you have to help me. Help me get out of this."

"Stacey, I'd like to, but I don't feel I can step in here. I barely know your parents."

"But you know me, and you're a doctor."

"Yes, but I'm not *your* doctor."

"*Please?*"

Dr Johanssen rose, too. She put her arm around me. "Let me think. I can't intervene directly, but before you leave for New York I'll—" She paused. "I promise I won't let you go to New York without doing *some-thing*. I just need to think. Fair enough?"

I nodded. "Thanks."

On my way home that afternoon, I vowed that I would not let Dr Barnes put me on any of his programmes. But I had only two weeks to figure out how to stop him.

8th
CHAPTER

For years, my parents have watched me go off to school wearing unusual clothing and accessories. They've let all sorts of things go by them unmentioned: the dinosaur on my beret, red sneakers covered with beads and glitter, leg warmers covered with footprints, plastic butterflies in my hair. For two weeks in New York I even wore red lace gloves with no fingertips.

But they'd never seen anything quite like what Kristy made the members of the Babysitters Club wear to school the Monday after Thanksgiving vacation. Even I was embarrassed. And poor Mary Anne looked as if she'd rather be stranded on a desert island with no hope of rescue.

Kristy had been busy during vacation. She'd made each of us a sandwich board to wear to school. The part that went over our fronts said: JOIN THE BEST CLUB

AROUND. The part that went over our backs said, in the block design Claudia had thought up for our fliers: THE BABYSITTERS CLUB.

"Put these on," said Kristy when we met on the street in front of my house. She was already wearing hers.

"Now?" I asked.

Kristy nodded. "We're going to look for new club members today and we might as well start on the way to school. Plenty of kids will see us."

"That's what I'm afraid of," whispered Claudia.

I shrugged. Then I put my notebook down. "Well, I'm ready."

Kristy helped me fit one of the ad boards over my head. I adjusted the strings on my shoulders. Then we helped Claudia and Mary Anne with theirs. Mary Anne's cheeks were burning bright red.

"Okay, let's go," I said. I waved self-consciously to my parents who were standing at the front door.

We marched off to Stoneybrook Middle School. All along the way, kids stopped and stared.

"I hope I don't see Trevor," Claudia murmured to me.

Trevor Sandbourne is Claudia's boyfriend. Sort of. He had taken Claudia to the Hallowe'en Hop and once they had gone to the pictures. I could understand why she

374

didn't want Trevor to see her.

"I know," I replied. "I hope we don't see Pete. Or Sam."

"Oh, no. Oh, *no*!" Claudia suddenly cried.

"What? Is it Trevor? Pete?"

"No. Look." Claudia pointed down the road behind us.

I turned around. A school bus was heading our way, loaded with high school students. They hung out of the windows and called to us as the bus passed by.

"Hey, hey!"

"Whoooo! The Babysitters Club!"

"Hey, girls, give me your number! *I* might need a sitter!"

Kristy held her head high and kept walking looking straight ahead.

"I'm dying, I'm dying," I whispered to Claudia. But I told myself that if I felt like a fool, it was for the sake of the club. And the club was worth it.

We reached school fifteen minutes before the first bell.

"Okay, now spread out," Kristy instructed.

"You mean we have to do this *alone*?" cried Mary Anne.

Kristy nodded. "Yes," she said firmly. "Walk around outside the building where kids can see you as they arrive at school. If anyone asks you questions, tell them about the club. Make sure they know they get to keep all the money they earn. And especially try to get some eighth-graders interested. Tell them the first meeting they'll attend will be on Wednesday."

We separated then and I wandered around by the main entrance to the school. Every single kid stared at me as he or she went by. Some pointed at the sign, then turned to speak to friends. A few laughed at me. But only three kids asked any questions.

"What's the Babysitters Club?" each one wanted to know.

I explained. I even told them about some of the kids we sat for.

"You ought to meet Charlotte Johanssen," I said to one girl (who, unfortunately, was a sixth-grader). "She's such a great little kid. She loves to be read to."

"You *read* to her?" said the girl incredulously. "Gosh, when I baby-sit, I use the time to watch TV."

"You do?" I said, just as incredulously. "What do the kids do while you're watching? Watch with you?"

She shrugged. "Sometimes. . . . I don't really care."

"Oh. . . ." She was not right for our club. I was glad she didn't ask any more questions.

The second kid, a boy, said, "You have to go to three meetings a week? I don't think I could fit that into—into my schedule."

The third kid was an eighth-grade girl who hated Liz Lewis. Perfect!

I told her about Charlotte.

I told her about David Michael.

I told her about Jamie.

I told her about Claire and Margo Pike and Nina and Eleanor Marshall.

Then I told her about the meetings and the notebook.

"It sounds like too much work," she said, and left.

The bell rang. The Babysitters Club walked into school together, Claudia, Mary Anne, and I taking our sandwich boards off as we went.

Kristy was grinning. "How did you guys do?" she asked.

"Terrible," I muttered.

"Rotten," said Claudia.

"Awful," said Mary Anne. "How come you're smiling?"

"Because I have good news!" announced Kristy. "But we won't discuss it in school. I'll tell you everything at our meeting this afternoon. . . . And put your signs back on. Wear them in the halls and the cafeteria today."

"In the cafeteria! How are we supposed to eat with these things on?" asked Claudia crossly.

"We can't sit down."

"Well, at least wear them in the lunch line."

"Oh, fine," grumbled Claudia, but she joined Mary Anne and me in placing the signs back over our shoulders.

I went to my locker, put my lunch away, and got out the books I'd need for the morning. Then I rushed off to English class. On the way, I passed Pete Black.

I nearly fainted.

Between maths class and advanced French (I was in the advanced class because in my school in New York we had been given French lessons since kindergarten) I passed Pete again.

He didn't look at me.

Had he really not seen me, or was he embarrassed by the sign?

It didn't matter, because at lunch time, when I approached our table in the cafeteria, still bravely wearing the sign, Pete looked up and smiled at me. "Let me help you take that thing off," he said. He lifted it over my shoulders.

"Embarrassed to be seen with me while I'm wearing it?" I asked.

Pete grinned. "Nah. . . . Well, maybe a little. But it takes guts to do what you're doing."

"Want to be in the club? We could use some boys."

Pete coughed. "*Me?* Take care of little kids?"

"Sure, why not?"

"I—I wouldn't know what to do."

"Well, never mind. It's okay."

We turned to our lunches. Pete is very

serious about food. We'd been eating for about five minutes when I noticed his face was turning red.

"Hey, what's wrong? Are you all right?" I thought he might be choking.

Pete swallowed. "Yeah, sure. I'm fine. But I have to ask you something."

"Okay."

"What I was wondering is . . . do you want to go the the Snowflake Dance with me?"

"That's not until December, is it?"

"This is December. It's December first."

"Oh, wow!" You're right." I was really flattered. Even if it was December, the dance was still almost three weeks away. And Pete was already asking me. "I'd love to go," I told him. "Thanks."

Across the table, Claudia was grinning at me.

Suddenly, I knew I wouldn't mind wearing the sandwich board any more.

Kristy was in a great mood at our meeting that afternoon. I couldn't see why. "*No*-body wanted to join the club," I told her. I was lounging on Claudia's bed, my feet propped up on the headboard. "It seems to be too much work."

"Yeah," said Claudia, who was sitting next to me. She rummaged around in her pillow case, trying to find some chocolate she'd hidden there.

"Yeah," agreed Mary Anne from her spot in the director's chair.

"But *I* got two new members," Kristy told us proudly. "And they're both eighth-graders."

"You're kidding!" I exclaimed. "That's super!"

"What are their names?" asked Claudia.

"Janet Gates and Lesley Howard."

Claudia frowned. "I thought they were friends of Liz's," she said slowly.

Kristy looked smug. "Not any more. They were part of the agency, but they dropped out. They didn't like it."

"Defectors," I said.

"Already?" asked Mary Anne.

"Yup," replied Kristy.

"Gosh, the agency must be pretty bad if kids are dropping out so soon," I said.

"Lesley said they didn't like having to give Liz and Michelle part of what they earned. Plus, Liz gave them really horrible kids to sit for. She kept all the nice, well-behaved ones for herself and Michelle."

"So they're coming to the next meeting?" asked Claudia.

"Yeah."

"But . . . something's wrong about this," said Mary Anne. "Something. . . . I know what it is. Remember when we were first starting the club and we were deciding whether to invite Stacey to join? We didn't know her, so we asked her all sorts of things about the baby-sitting she did in New York. We wanted a club of *good* baby-sitters. Dedicated baby-sitters. Do you know anything about Janet and Lesley, Kristy?"

"Well, no," she admitted.

"And you've already told them they can be members?"

"Yes. . . ."

"Gosh, I don't know."

"It seems risky," I said.

Kristy looked at us uncomfortably. "Well, it's too late now. We'll just have to take our chances."

Claudia found several pieces of butterscotch in her pillowcase and handed them to Kristy and Mary Anne. They unwrapped them and began crunching away.

"Well, there's one good thing," I spoke up.

"What?" everybody asked eagerly.

"If the agency is as horrible as Janet and Lesley say, maybe it won't last long."

"Yeah," agreed the others.

We sat quietly, and after a moment I realized that the four of us were staring at the phone. "I wonder if we could make it ring if we all concentrated on it," I said. We tried, but nothing happened.

At six o'clock, when the meeting ended, we hadn't had a single Babysitters Club call.

9th CHAPTER

The next afternoon, since none of us had a baby-sitting job and we were very bored, we went over to the Thomases' house. Kristy called Mrs Newton, who was home from the hospital, and asked if we could visit them and see the new baby. When she said yes, we were really excited.

"Oh, goody!" exclaimed Kristy after she'd hung up the phone. "I have a present for the baby, and one for Jamie, too."

"So do I," I said.

"So do I," said Claudia.

"So do I," said Mary Anne.

"Are they wrapped?" asked Claudia.

"No," we answered.

"Good. Go get your presents and meet me in my room. I've got great stuff for gift-wrapping."

When we were gathered in Claudia's room, we spread out our presents. We all began to squeal, "Oh, that's so *cute*!"

Kristy had got a little toy car for Jamie and a rattle shaped like a duck for Lucy. Claudia had bought Jamie a dinosaur and had painted a picture of kittens for Mrs Newton to hang in the baby's room. I had bought two books: a paperback called *Mike Mulligan and his Steam Shovel* for Jamie, and *Pat the Bunny* for Lucy.

Mary Anne's gifts were the best of all: a red ski hat for Jamie and a little pink hat for the baby.

"I made them," she said shyly. "Can you tell?"

"You're kidding!" I exclaimed. "You *made* those?"

"Then you couldn't tell?"

"No way!"

"Mary Anne, I didn't know you could knit," said Kristy.

Mary Anne glanced at Claudia, who smiled at her.

"Mimi's teaching her," said Claudia. "She's been dying to teach someone, but Janine and I aren't interested."

"She remembers my mother," added Mary Anne. "She tells me about her while I work."

"That's—that's great," I said. (Was that what I was supposed to say?)

Mary Anne brightened. "She's going to help me make a scarf for my father."

"Wow!" We were all impressed.

Claudia hauled a big square box out of her cupboard. "Okay, go to town," she said.

We looked in the box. It was jammed with stuff Claudia had collected over the years: plastic flowers, paper hearts, beads, bows, ribbons, felt animals. "Those are package decorations," she told us. "We can make our own wrapping paper with these." She opened a shoe box that was full of rubber stamps. "See? I've got four ink pads in different colours. You can stamp this white paper to make any design you want. Then we'll decorate the packages with the other stuff."

We got to work. I printed red hearts and blue flowers on Lucy's paper, and big green frogs saying "Ribbit!" on Jamie's paper. When we were finished, we admired our packages briefly, and then ran to the Newtons' house.

Jamie answered the door. "Hi," he greeted us.

Mrs Newton appeared behind him. "Hello, there! Oh, I'm so glad to see you! Jamie has missed you, and I'm dying for you to meet Lucy. Come inside."

We stepped through the door. I was surprised to see that Mrs Newton still looked, well, fat. Not pregnant exactly, but not the way I'd thought she would look after the baby was born.

"Oh, you girls are so sweet. You've brought gifts. You didn't have to do that."

"We know," said Kristy, grinning.

"We just wanted to," I added.

"Yeah," said Mary Anne. "Babies are special."

Jamie eyed the presents, then glanced at his mother. "Are any of those for me?"

"Jamie! It's not polite to ask!" Mrs Newton turned to us. "I'm sorry. The last week has been difficult. Jamie is a bit J-E-A-L-O-U-S," she spelled. "L-U-C-Y had been given a lot of P-R-E-S-E-N-T-S."

"Well, you're in luck, Jamie," said Claudia. "Four of these are for you."

"Four!" cried Jamie. We didn't make him wait. We handed him the presents and he tore into them.

"What do you say?" prompted Mrs Newton.

"Thank you," replied Jamie automatically. He was wearing the hat, and trying to read the book and play with the toys at the same time.

Then we gave Mrs Newton Lucy's gifts.

"Let's go and peek at the baby before I open them," she said. "I wish Lucy were awake so you could hold her, but she's still napping."

She led us upstairs and into the little room that had been fixed up for Lucy. A big white crib stood in one corner, but Lucy was asleep in a blue basket near the door. "She's too little for the crib," Mrs Newton whispered. "Babies feel more secure in a small bed."

The members of the Babysitters Club silently surrounded the basket and peered inside.

"Ohhh," I breathed.

"She's so *little*," whispered Mary Anne.

She certainly was. I guess I hadn't realized just how little a newborn baby really is.

"Can I touch her?" I asked Mrs Newton softly.

She nodded.

I leaned over and ran my finger along one of Lucy's tiny hands. It was soft as silk, and perfect: four little fingers and a thumb, each ending in a fingernail no bigger than a speck. I breathed in. Lucy smelled sweet, like baby powder and milk. I ran my hand lightly over the fine dark hair on her head. She stirred then opened her eyes just long enough for me to see that they were a deep blue. Then she closed them again.

I glanced up. Claudia, Kristy, and Mary Anne looked enchanted.

A few moments later we were back downstairs, sitting in the living room while Mrs Newton opened the baby presents. She exclaimed over each one and commented on the original wrapping.

"Do you think the hat will fit?" Mary Anne asked anxiously.

"In a few weeks it should be just right."

Mary Anne let out a sigh of relief.

"Mrs Newton?" Kristy said. "Could I

ask you something?"

"Of course."

Suddenly my stomach lurched. I had this horrible feeling I knew what Kristy was going to ask. I looked over at Claudia and found that she was already looking at me. Oh, no, her eyes seemed to be saying, I can't believe she's going to bring this up *now*.

But she did.

"I'm not sure how to say this," Kristy began, "but when Jamie was at our house last week, he said we wouldn't be baby-sitting for him any more. I mean, no—He said he heard you on the phone with Liz Lewis from the Baby-sitters Agency. Is—? Can we still—?" Kristy didn't know how to finish what she had started.

Mrs Newton's face was flushed with embarrassment.

I was pretty sure mine was, too. It felt very hot.

"I guess I should have told you," said Mrs Newton. "I knew how excited you were about the new baby. And of course you'll always be our favourite sitters. It's just that a baby is so delicate and fragile, and needs extra-special care—"

"But we're responsible," protested Kristy.

"I've taken care of babies before," I added.

"Newborns?" asked Mrs Newton.

"Well, one was ten months and the other was eight months."

"That makes a big difference," she said. "There's even a big difference between a three-month-old baby and a newborn. Anyway, what I was going to say, is that for the next few months, I'll simply feel more comfortable leaving Lucy with an older sitter. The times when I take Lucy with me and there's just Jamie to sit for, I'll be glad to use the Babysitters Club."

"I can understand that," Claudia said slowly.

"I'm glad you still want us to sit for Jamie," said Kristy.

"And when Lucy is older, I hope you'll be my regular sitters again," added Mrs Newton.

"Oh, definitely!" I said, but I didn't feel nearly as cheerful as I sounded. Nothing seemed to be going our way any more.

After school the next day, I met Janet and Lesley for the first time. They arrived promptly at five-thirty for our Wednesday meeting of the Babysitters Club.

I studied them critically. Of course, they were already members of the club, but I couldn't resist asking them a few questions.

"Have you done a lot of baby-sitting?" I asked Janet.

"Oh, tons," she replied. She was chewing a wad of gum and she cracked it loudly.

"You, too?" I asked Lesley.

Lesley looked bored. She brushed her

shaggy hair out of her face. I noticed that she was wearing makeup. A lot of it.

"Sure," she replied. She glanced at Janet and they exchanged smiles.

"Where?" asked Mary Anne. I was surprised to see her jumping in, but I knew she was concerned about our reputation.

"Over on the other side of town," replied Janet. (Crack, crack. Snap.) "You probably wouldn't know any of the people."

"How old's the youngest kid you ever sat for?" asked Claudia.

"About nine months," said Lesley.

"Same (crack) here," said Janet.

Kristy was watching us nervously, her eyes travelling back and forth between the new members of the club and the old members.

"How many kids can you sit for at one time?" I wanted to know.

"Oh, three or four, I guess," answered Lesley.

"Yeah," said Janet. (Crack, snap.)

Kristy must have decided it was time to impress us. "How late can you stay out?" she asked.

"Eleven o'clock on weekdays," they replied at the same time.

"On Friday and Saturday nights (crack) I can stay out until midnight (snap)," added Janet.

"I can stay out until any hour on the weekend as long as I tell my mum first," said Lesley.

My jaw dropped open. "How old are you?"

"Fourteen," she replied.

"I'm thirteen," said Janet.

I began to feel the tiniest bit impressed.

Kristy looked around triumphantly. "I think what we ought to do now is let our clients know about our new members." She pulled a copy of our old Babysitters Club flier out of a folder she was carrying. "We'll add Janet and Lesley's names and ages to this, and the times when we can sit. Then my mum will Xerox the new version of the flier and we'll distribute the copies as soon as possible. Who can help me tomorrow after school?"

"I can," said Claudia, Mary Anne, and I.

We looked at Janet and Lesley. They were looking at each other.

"Well," said Janet (crackle, crackle), "we'd like to help you, but we have baby-sitting jobs tomorrow (crack). You know, previous commitments."

Kristy glanced at me as if to say, See how responsible they are?

"All right," said Kristy. "Here's the plan of action. Tomorrow, we distribute fliers. We'll also call our best customers personally to tell them the news. Friday, we meet again."

We followed Kristy's plan. And at the Friday meeting we got four baby-sitting jobs. Two were last-minute late-night ones for Janet and Lesley over the weekend. We couldn't wait for our Monday meeting to see how things had gone.

The Babysitters Club seemed to be back on its feet.

10th CHAPTER

Monday, December 8

Today Kristy, Stacey & Mary Anne all arrived early for our Baby-Sitters Club meeting. We were all really excited to find out how Janet and Lesley's sitting jobs had gone on Saturday. When it was 5:30 we kept expecting the doorbell to ring any second. But it didn't. Soon it was 5:50. Where were they? Kristy was getting worried. Write this down in our notebook, somebody, she said. Something's wrong. Unfortunately, Kristy was right. It turned out that something was very very wrong. And it was part of the awful thing with the Baby-Sitters Agency.

Wow. What happened on Monday was one of the worst events in the war between the

Babysitters Club and the Baby-sitters Agency. As Claudia mentioned, the four original club members gathered early for our Monday meeting. We couldn't wait to talk to Janet and Lesley.

Despite the fact that Claudia's digital clock flipped to 5.35 and the new members hadn't shown up yet, the meeting got off to a good start. First Mrs Marshall called, needing a sitter for Wednesday afternoon. Mary Anne took the job. Then Watson, Kristy's future stepfather, needed a sitter for an early evening job on Wednesday. Kristy took that job, of course. Then Mrs Newton called! She wanted someone to watch Jamie on Wednesday afternoon while she took Lucy to the paediatrician for a check-up. I took that job, since Claudia has art lessons on Wednesdays. We were so busy taking calls that it was 5.50 before we looked at the clock again and realized Janet and Lesley were late.

"They could have at least called to say they weren't going to make the meeting this afternoon," I pointed out.

Even Kristy looked miffed. "I saw Janet in school today, and she didn't say anything about not coming."

"I think it's weird that *neither* of them showed up," said Mary Anne. "What could have happened to make them both late?"

Kristy shrugged. "Maybe they just forgot."

"We've told them about meetings a million times," said Claudia. "If they forgot, then they're pretty irresponsible."

"Well, I'll call them," said Kristy. She knew something was wrong then, because that was when she told Claudia to write about the incident in our notebook.

"No, I'll call them," I said. "I want to know who they think they are!"

"Don't get mad," said Kristy. "It won't help. *I'll call*. I'm the chairman."

"No, I want to c—"

The phone rang then. Kristy and I both lunged for it, but Mary Anne was sitting practically on top of it. She beat us to it.

"Hello, the Babysitters Club," she said. ". . . No, this is Mary Anne Spier. Can I help you? Oh, hi, Mr Kelly. . . . She *didn't*?"

Kristy and Claudia and I jerked to attention. The Kellys were the new family Lesley had arranged to sit for on Saturday night. They had contacted the club after we'd sent around our updated fliers.

"Mr Kelly," Mary Anne was saying, "I'm terribly sorry. I don't know what happened. . . . Well, I'd like to, but she's not here right now. I guess you could call her at home. . . . Oh, I see. Well, would you like to speak to our chairman? . . . Okay. . . . Sure. And I—I'm really sorry."

Mary Anne's face was flaming. She cupped her hand over the mouthpiece, and

394

as she passed the receiver to Kristy she whispered, "Lesley never showed up on Saturday. She didn't even bother to call the Kellys."

Kristy took the phone, her eyes closed, steeling herself for the conversation with Mr Kelly. "Kristy Thomas here," she said after a moment, "club chairman. . . . Yes, Mary Anne just mentioned that. I feel terrible. Lesley never told *me* she wasn't going to be able to keep her appointment with you. If she had, I would have sent over one of our other fine sitters. . . . I hope you can accept our apologies. . . . Sure. . . . Sure. Okay, goodbye."

Kristy hung up the phone. I couldn't tell whether she was angry or scared or embarrassed. Maybe she was all three. She kept still for so long that at last I said, "He was really mad, right?"

"Yup. He and his wife had tickets to see his wife's brother perform in a concert in Stamford. When Lesley didn't show up he called her house, but no one was home. The Kellys had to scramble around trying to get someone to watch their kids. At last they left them with a neighbour, but by the time they reached the concert hall, they'd missed twenty minutes of the concert."

"Uh-oh," said Claudia.

"Why didn't they just call one of us?" I asked.

"Simple," snapped Kristy. "They didn't

trust us, and why should they? Mr Kelly was only calling now to make sure we knew what Lesley had done. I have a feeling the Kellys won't be calling the Babysitters Club again."

"Oh, great," I said, letting out a breath I hadn't even realized I'd been holding. "Wait until word gets around about *this*."

The phone rang again. Nobody made a move to answer it. Finally, I picked it up on the third ring. "Hello, the Babysitters Club," I said glumly. "Stacey McGill speaking. . . . Yes? . . . Oh, no, you're *kidding*! I mean, I'm sorry, I'm so sorry. We had no idea. Maybe you'd like to talk to our chairman. . . . Okay, hold on." I handed Kristy the phone, whispering, "I don't believe it. This is Ms Jaydell. You know, the other new client? The woman *Janet* was supposed to sit for? Janet didn't show up, either."

It was Kristy's turn to be furious. She jerked the phone to her ear, eyes flashing, and had to unclench her jaw before saying (fairly civilly), "Kristin Thomas speaking."

I'd seen Kristy mad before, but never *that* mad.

She carried on pretty much the same conversation with Ms Jaydell that she'd had with Mr Kelly a few minutes earlier. The only difference was that Ms. Jaydell and her husband hadn't been able to find another sitter, and had missed out on a cocktail party.

When Kristy hung up the phone, she burst into tears. It was the first time I'd ever seen her cry.

"Well, that does it," I said, handing her a tissue from the table by Claudia's bed. "What are Janet and Lesley's phone numbers? I'm going to call them right now. They're really hurting us."

"No," said Kristy, wiping her eyes. "Don't call them. I want to confront them face-to-face. We'll talk to them in school tomorrow. This wasn't any accident. They missed those jobs on purpose. I'm sure of it."

"But why?" asked Claudia.

"Beats me," said Kristy. Who's going to help me face those traitors tomorrow?"

"I am!" I said.

"I am!" said Claudia.

We looked at Mary Anne. "Couldn't we confront them over the phone?" she asked.

"Over the phone is not a confrontation," I said firmly.

"We have to be face-to-face."

"We do?"

"Yes, we do."

"*All* of us," added Kristy. "The whole club. United."

"All right," said Mary Anne at last.

None of us were looking forward to school

the next day. We walked together in the morning, travelling about as fast as snails.

"When are we going to confront them?" I asked Kristy as we reached Stoneybrook Middle School.

"Yeah," said Claudia. "We don't have any classes with them."

"We're going to confront them right now," Kristy replied. "I know where their classrooms are. We're going to wait for them."

"An ambush," said Mary Anne.

Janet and Lesley were not in the same classroom, but the rooms were just across the hall from each other. Kristy and Mary Anne waited by Janet's room; Claudia and I waited by Lesley's.

After about five minutes of standing around, I spotted them down the hall. "Psst! Kristy!" I said. "Here they come. Both of them."

"Hey," Claudia whispered to me. "Look who's with them."

I looked. It was Liz Lewis. "I thought they didn't like Liz," I said.

"I know." Claudia frowned.

We watched the girls stop for a moment, talking earnestly. Then Liz waved to them and disappeared into a classroom.

Janet and Lesley saw us before they reached their classrooms. They nudged each other, laughing.

The members of the Babysitters Club

converged on them.

"Where were you yesterday?" Kristy demanded.

"Hey (snap, snap), what kind of greeting is that?" asked Janet. She must have had twelve pieces of gum in her mouth.

"I'm not kidding," said Kristy. "I want to know where you were, and I want to know why you didn't show up for your Saturday sitting jobs. Our club is known for responsible baby-sitters."

"So what?" said Lesley.

"So what!" exclaimed Kristy. "You're giving us a bad reputation. We're going to have to ask you to leave the club."

"Fine with us," replied Janet. "We," she added with a smirk, "are members of the Baby-sitters *Agency*." She and Lesley burst into hysterical laughter.

"But—but—" stammered Kristy.

"We had you completely fooled!"

"You're rats!" I cried suddenly. "Both of you. You did this to make us look bad! That's—it's—it's *dirty*. It's not fair."

Janet and Lesley couldn't stop laughing. And I couldn't stop accusing. "You're liars! And—and dirty businesswomen!"

"Whoa," said Lesley. "Get that. Dirty businesswomen. Pretty high-class talk."

"And probably *rotten* baby-sitters," Kristy added.

Lesley took some offence at that. "We are *not* rotten baby-sitters," she said, bristling.

"Well, what do you call a baby-sitter who doesn't show up for a job, and doesn't call the parents to explain why?"

"Hmm," said Lesley. "Janet, what would you call that sitter?"

"I'd call her anything except late for dinner!"

Lesley and Janet doubled over with laughter at their stupid joke.

"Shut up! Shut up!" cried Kristy. "I hope you realize you're in big trouble."

"With who?" said Janet, still laughing.

"With . . . with the parents. I'm going to call them and tell them exactly what happened. Then they'll call their friends, and their friends will call *their* friends. Word will get around. You'll be sorry.

At last the girls stopped laughing. "You wouldn't dare," said Janet. At the same time Lesley said, "No, *you'll* be sorry, tattletale."

"Me? Why should I be sorry?" asked Kristy.

"Because," replied Lesley, "Liz and Michelle will be interested in your plans. They'll just have to work a little harder to be the best sitting agency in town. But they won't mind that."

"You—" exclaimed Kristy, simmering "—you are *pigs*!"

Janet snapped her gum. "Sorry, *kids*." She and Lesley separated and walked into their classrooms.

400

Kristy, Claudia, Mary Anne, and I were left standing in the hall. For the second time in two days, Kristy began to cry. The rest of us surrounded her and walked her into the nearest girls' toilet. It was pretty crowded, but we huddled in a corner and no one paid much attention to us.

"I'm so embarrassed," Kristy wailed. "It *isn't* fair. That was a really rotten trick. Besides, a baby-sitting club was *my* idea, not Liz's. We worked so *hard* on our club. And even when the agency started up, we never tried to hurt them. We just tried to protect what we had." She blew her nose on a paper towel. "Now they're purposely trying to beat us out."

"So Liz put Janet and Lesley up to what they did," I said slowly.

Kristy nodded. "Yes. And it's all my fault for being so stupid about taking on new members. Mary Anne was right. I should have checked on them."

"Well," said Claudia, "I agree that what the agency is doing to us is really mean. But I think what we have to do is just keep going—the four of us. Okay, so we can't stay out late. So we're only twelve years old. Most of our clients like us a lot. We'll just go on being as responsible and good with children and —and—what's that word that means you sort of adjust yourself to whatever people need?"

"Flexible?" suggested Mary Anne.

"Almost," Claudia replied. "That's not the word, but it's close."

"I know what you mean," said Kristy. "I guess you're right. Anyway, I *am* going to explain things to Mr Kelly and Ms Jaydell."

"And," I added frantically, "there's always lower rates and housework and special deals."

"No," said Kristy. "I've decided that's not the way to go. The club will survive, but we don't want to become slaves. Besides, I can't deal with any of that stuff right now. We've got to think of ways to prove that *we're* better than the agency."

With that, the bell rang, and the Babysitters Club silently left the girls' toilet.

11th CHAPTER

The agency had lit a fire under Kristy. She did call the Kellys and the Jaydells to explain what had happened. They were interested and seemed somewhat friendlier, but Kristy still wasn't sure whether they'd call on the club again. At least the truth had been told.

Then Kristy made plans for us to advertise our club out at Washington Mall. She was already at work on new sandwich boards. Each one would carry a different slogan. We helped Kristy make them up. They were:

YOUNGER IS BETTER
RESPONSIBILITY + PUNCTUALITY =
THE BABYSITTERS CLUB
THE FIRST AND FINEST BABY-SITTING
SERVICE
QUALITY CARE FOR KIDS

The first trip to the mall was scheduled for the weekend, but I wouldn't be able to go. I'd be suffering torture at the hands of Dr Barnes.

On Wednesday afternoon, I baby-sat for Jamie. Something was bothering him. He moped around as if he'd lost his best friend. He had greeted me cheerfully enough when I arrived, but as soon as Mrs Newton carried a bundled-up Lucy out the back door, his face fell. He wandered into the playroom, put on the TV, and flung himself onto the couch. He didn't even check to see what was on the channel the television was tuned to. Usually he wouldn't watch anything except *Sesame Street* or *Mister Rogers' Neighbourhood*.

I thought I knew what was wrong. "It must be kind of tough having a new baby at your house," I suggested.

Jamie shrugged. "It's okay."

"I bet she cries a lot."

"Not too much. If Mummy rocks her, she stops."

I thought for a moment. "I remember when my friend Allison's baby sister was born. Allison hated her."

Jamie looked surprised. "I don't hate Lucy," he said.

"Everything is A-OK with the baby?"

Jamie nodded.

"You seem kind of sad," I said after a

while. Jamie let out a sigh that indicated he was carrying the weight of the entire world on his shoulders. "Baby-sitters used to be fun," he said.

I frowned. "What do you mean?"

"Baby-sitters used to play games with me and push me on the swings and colour monster pictures and read me stories."

I couldn't get away from the Lucy angle. "And now they're too busy taking care of the baby?"

"No. Too busy watching TV. . . . What are *you* going to watch this afternoon?"

"Me? I'm not going to watch TV. I was going to ask you if you wanted to read *Where the Wild Things Are* and draw pictures of Max's monsters."

Jamie perked up.

"Plus, I brought the Kid-Kit with me."

"You *did*! I didn't see. Where is it?"

"It's in the living room. But wait a second, Jamie. Tell me more about your baby-sitters. Are you saying that all they do is watch TV?"

"And they"—he leaned over and began to whisper—"they have accidents."

"Accidents?" I whispered back.

"Yeah."

"What kinds of accidents?"

He got up and led me across the room to a chair. "Like this," he whispered. He poked at something on the cushion.

I looked at it closely. It was a burn mark.

In fact, it was a hole. My eyes widened. "One of your sitters did that?" I asked.

Jamie nodded. "With a—a cigarette." He said "cigarette" as if it were a dirty word. Neither of his parents is a smoker.

"Gosh," I said. "Anything else?"

"Sometimes they talk on the phone. They talk longer than Mummy and Daddy do. . . . Stacey?"

"Yeah?"

"What's a boyfriend?"

I gulped. I hadn't been prepared for that question. "Well," I said thoughtfully, "it's, um, it's a friend who's a boy."

"Am I your boyfriend?" asked Jamie.

"Not exactly. Listen, Jamie. Who baby-sits for you now? Do you know their names?"

Jamie scrunched up his face. "Tammy," he said. "And Barbara. And a boy."

I didn't know Tammy and Barbara or any boy sitters. Maybe they were in high school.

"Well, you know what?" I said. "If you don't like your sitters, you should tell your mummy. Tell her what you told me, that all they do is watch TV and talk on the phone. And show her the chair. Okay? Can you do that?" I wanted to help the Babysitters Club, but I also truly hated to see Jamie so sad.

"Yup."

"Good boy. Now—you don't *really* want to watch *Gilligan's Island*, do you?" I said, looking at the blaring television set.

"Yuck." Jamie jumped up and switched it off.

"What'll it be?" I asked. "*Wild Things* or the Kid-Kit?"

"Kid-Kit!"

"You got it." I retrieved the Kid-Kit, and pulled out the things that would interest an almost-four-year-old. Jamie played happily until Mrs Newton and Lucy returned.

When I got home that afternoon, I heard the phone ringing. Apparently Mum was out. I dashed into the kitchen and picked up the receiver. "Hello?"

"Hello, Stacey?"

"Yes?"

"Oh, hi. It's Dr Johanssen. I was about to hang up."

"Sorry," I said. "I just got home."

"Well, listen, I know your Babysitters Club meets in a little while, but I thought I'd try to catch you now. I need a sitter tonight. It's last minute, but it won't be too late, and Charlotte's been asking for you."

"She has?" I said, feeling very pleased.

"Endlessly," said Dr Johanssen cheerfully. "Can you come over at seven?"

"Sure!" I replied. (Ordinarily, I'm not allowed to sit both the afternoon and the evening of a school day, but I didn't have much homework, so I knew it would be all right.)

"Terrific. We'll see you then," said Dr Johanssen.

" 'Bye." We hung up.

I was pleased for two reasons. Not only was I delighted to have a night job at the Johanssens' (I hadn't had one in quite a while), but I was working on a plan regarding the New York trip, and I needed to discuss something with Dr Johanssen. I also needed her to answer some questions.

My plan was this: I'd let Mum and Dad take me to their "doctor" on Saturday. I knew what that visit would be like: a lot of questions, especially about my diet and insulin and my medical history, and then maybe a few quick tests, followed by plans for the work-up in his clinic on Monday and Tuesday. Just preliminary stuff. I'd been through it all before. Then I would tell my parents I'd been researching diabetes on my own and that I knew of a doctor *I* wanted to see. That was where Dr Johanssen came in. I needed her to recommend someone *sensible* to me. Someone who would think that we were handling my disease just fine. Someone like Dr Werner. Furthermore, the someone needed a fancy office and *lots* of diplomas.

After supper that night, I got the Kid-Kit and a torch and took the shortcut through our neighbours' back yards to the Johanssens'. Dr Johanssen met me at the front door.

"Hi, Stacey," she said. "I'm glad you could come." She closed the door behind me and took my coat. Then she glanced over her shoulder at Charlotte who was doing her homework at the kitchen table. Dr Johanssen lowered her voice. "Charlotte has been in a funny mood lately," she told me. "Very quiet and slightly listless. She says she feels fine, so something's going on that she's not talking about. I have a feeling it's school-related, and I've arranged a conference with her teacher. I just wanted you to know so that you won't worry if she seems out of sorts tonight."

"Okay," I replied.

"Mr Johanssen is working late tonight," Charlotte's mother continued, "and I have a PTA meeting. We'll both be back before nine."

"All right. . . . Dr Johanssen, when you come home, could I talk to you? We're leaving for New York on Saturday, and I have an idea."

"Certainly, honey. There's something I wanted to tell you, anyway." Dr Johanssen headed into the kitchen. "Well, sweetie," she said to Charlotte, "I won't be late. Finish your homework, and then you can have fun with Stacey until Daddy and I get home. . . . Okay?"

Charlotte nodded.

" 'Bye, honey."

" 'Bye." Charlotte barely looked up.

I sat down next to her as her mother left the house. "Gosh, homework in second grade. That's pretty important. *I* didn't have homework in second grade."

"It's just two stupid worksheets," said Charlotte.

"Do you need any help with them?"

She shook her head. "They're easy. It's stupid, stupid, homework."

"Well, if it's easy, it won't take you long to finish, right?"

"What do you care?"

"Charlotte!" I exclaimed. "Why are you talking to me like that? If you're mad, you better tell me what I did wrong, because I'm not a mindreader."

Charlotte slouched over her worksheets. "I'm not mad."

"Well, you sound mad." I felt as if I were having a fight with Laine Cummings. "I only wanted to know because when you finish, we can read some of *The Cricket in Times Square*."

"Oh, *sure*," she said sarcastically.

"Charlotte, what is the matter with you? Your mother said you wanted me to sit for you."

"I wanted you to come over. I didn't want you to baby-sit."

"I don't think I understand."

"Stacey, how come you baby-sit for me?"

"Because I like to," I replied. "You're one of my favourite kids."

Charlotte smiled vaguely. Then she asked, "Why do you *really* sit?"

"Because I like kids. And when I moved here, I wanted to meet people."

"What about the money?"

Money? What had made Charlotte think about *that*? "Well, of course the money's nice. I like to earn money."

"I thought so."

"But I like you, too. I wouldn't baby-sit for just anybody. And I'll tell you something. If your mum and dad called me and said, 'We need you to sit for Charlotte tonight, but we're broke and we can't pay you,' I'd come anyway."

"You would?"

"Yes. I *told* you I like you."

"Some baby-sitters only sit because they want money. They don't care about the kids."

"*Which* baby-sitters?" I asked.

"Mmnns," mumbled Charlotte.

"What?"

"My new ones," she said quietly.

"Who are your new ones?"

"Michelle Patterson, Lesley somebody, and Cathy Morris."

"They all told you that?"

"No. Ellie Morris told me."

"Who's Ellie Morris?"

"Cathy's sister. She's in my class. She hates me."

Aha, I thought.

Charlotte looked at me sadly. "Ellie said, 'Oh, Charlotte, you are the teacher's pet, teacher's pet,' and I said, 'I am not,' and she said, 'Are too, and you don't have any friends.' And I said, 'I have baby-sitters. They're my friends.' And she said, 'They are not. My sister Cathy doesn't like you.' And I said, 'Then how come she sits for me?' And she said, 'Because your parents pay her a lot of money, stupid.' "

I was beginning to put the pieces together. Charlotte didn't have friends of her own age; that much I knew. Apparently, she thought her baby-sitters were her friends, though. Then Ellie had burst her bubble. Yet Charlotte had been asking for me. If I had come over just to visit (not to baby-sit), it would have proved I truly was a friend. No wonder she was upset.

"Hey, Char," I said, "remember when we gave Jamie Newton the Big Brother Party? I invited you. I wasn't baby-sitting for you then."

"Yeah . . ." said Charlotte slowly.

"Also, what do Michelle and Lesley and Cathy do when they baby-sit for you?"

"Watch TV. Talk on the phone. Once Lesley brought her boyfriend over." I raised my eyebrows. "Cathy always does her homework, but she won't help me with

412

mine. She says, 'I'm too busy now.' "

"What do *I* do when I baby-sit?"

"Well, you bring the Kid-Kit. We read stories and take walks and play games."

"That's being a friend, isn't it?" I asked.

Suddenly Charlotte gave me a fierce hug. "*Yes*," she said, "I'm sorry I was cross."

"That's all right." I made a mental note to help Charlotte make some friends—some *seven*-year-old friends—in the neighbourhood. One of the Pikes was seven, I thought. Then I told her what I had told Jamie that afternoon—that if she didn't like her new sitters, she should talk to her parents. In particular, she should mention that Lesley had invited her boyfriend over.

By the time Dr Johanssen returned, Charlotte seemed like her old self.

And Charlotte's mother was very helpful. "It's funny," she said when I asked about a doctor. "You know what I was going to tell you? I was going to tell you about this very sensible doctor in New York. I guess we were thinking along the same lines."

I asked about the doctor's office and whether he had a lot of diplomas. He seemed to fit the bill. "Do you think I could get an appointment with him on Saturday afternoon?" I asked. "That's just three days away."

"I'll pull a few strings," said Dr Johanssen. "And I'd better explain things to your parents."

"Oh, no. Please don't!" I cried. "It has to be a surprise. Otherwise it'll never work."

"Well, how about if I write a note to your parents? You can give it to them over the weekend—before you see the doctor."

"All right," I said at last. That wasn't quite what I had planned on, but I was willing to compromise. I didn't want Dr Johanssen to get in any trouble. "That's great," I said, and thanked her.

I ran home feeling excited.

My plan was underway.

12th CHAPTER

Thursday, December 11

Surprise! Today Stacey called an emergency club meeting for lunch-time. That was unexpected for two reasons. First of all, Kristy had said no more club business in school. Second, Kristy calls emergency meetings at the drop of a hat, but no other member has ever called one. Stacey called one, though, and it was a good thing she did, because what she told us got the club ready for the final battle in the war against the Baby-sitters Agency.

I read what Mary Anne wrote in our notebook about battles and wars, and I think she was being overly dramatic.

415

However, she was right—it was good that we held that meeting. It started us thinking about some important things.

Finding a place to hold the meeting turned out to be a problem. Kristy acted as if the school were bugged or something.

"How about at a separate table in the cafeteria?" Claudia suggested.

"Are you kidding? Never!" said Kristy. "Someone's *sure* to overhear us."

"Is there an empty classroom we could sit in?" asked Mary Anne.

Kristy rejected the idea. "It's too easy for someone to stand outside the door and eavesdrop."

"I guess the girls' toilet would—"

"No way. You just hide in one of the cubicles and stand on the toilet. No one knows you're there. You could hear everything."

"Well, what about the playground?" I said. "We'll go off by ourselves, but we'll stand out in the open. That way no one can sneak up on us, and we can move away if anyone comes too close."

That was what we decided to do. We ate lunch quickly and gathered on the playground. It had snowed the night before and there were about three inches covering the ground. My feet were blocks of ice before we even started talking. (In New York City, three inches of snow wouldn't bother to stick. The flakes would melt as soon as they touched the pavement.)

"Okay, Stacey," said Kristy. "So why did you call this meeting?"

"Because we've got a problem."

"Another one?"

"A big one. But it might end up working out well for us," I said.

"That would be a switch," Claudia commented.

"What happened," I began, tucking my mittened hands under my arms in an effort to thaw out my fingers, which were as cold as my toes, "was that I baby-sat twice yesterday. Remember, I told you at the meeting that I had sat for Jamie and he was upset about his new sitters?"

The girls nodded.

"Well, I forgot to tell you that I told Jamie to tell his mother if he doesn't like the sitters. I mean, we can't say anything to the parents, but the kids we sit for can."

"Oh, good idea," remarked Kristy.

"And in the evening I sat for Charlotte, and she was upset, too. So I told *her* to talk to *her* parents. I think that from now on, we should watch for signs that the kids we take care of aren't happy with the Baby-sitters Agency. Then we should encourage them to speak up. They have the right."

The other club members agreed with that wholeheartedly.

We also agreed that agency sitters were inferior to club sitters. We were quality, and they were. . . . Well, they were not. But we weren't prepared for what we saw on our way home from school that afternoon.

The weather was awful. The sky was grey and the air was still cold and windy. It was a raw day. The unploughed streets had turned to beds of icy slush. We were all freezing cold and my teeth were chattering. As we rounded the corner to the street that Kristy, Claudia, and Mary Anne live on, we almost bumped into Jamie Newton. He was standing by himself on the narrow strip of grass that runs between the sidewalk and the street.

"Hi-hi!" Jamie called.

"Jamie!" Kristy exclaimed. "What are you doing here?"

"Playing," he replied.

"Well, you're much too near the street. Aren't you supposed to be in your backyard?" She looked at the rest of us as if to say, what is *wrong* with Mrs Newton?

"And where are your mittens, Jamie?" I added. "And your hat? It's freezing out here. Is your mother very busy with Lucy today?"

Jamie shook his head. "She's at a meeting. Lucy is asleep."

A car came whizzing down the street then. It sprayed us with slush. I shivered, trying not to think about what might have happened if Jamie had been playing *in* the street.

"Jamie," Mary Anne said suddenly, "do you have a baby-sitter today?"

"Yup."

"What's her name?"

"Barb—no, Cathy."

"Cathy Morris?" I asked.

"Yup."

"Does she know you're out here?" Kristy asked.

Jamie shrugged. "She said I could play outside."

I turned to the club members. "What do you think we should do?" I asked them.

"I'm not sure," Kristy answered slowly.

"Look," I said, kneeling down to Jamie's level. "Can you do two special things? Just for us?"

"Yes," he replied solemnly.

"Good boy. The first thing is to go inside and find your hat and mittens. If you can't reach them, ask Cathy for help. But don't go outdoors without them, okay?"

"Yes."

"The second thing is to play out back if you want to be outdoors. It's dangerous here by the street. Play on your swing, okay?"

"Yes."

We watched Jamie run across his lawn and through his front door before we went on our way.

"Wow," said Kristy. "This is serious. That baby-sitter, whoever the so-called agency found for the Newtons, lets *three-year-olds* play outside on their own. Do you know what could have happened to Jamie?"

"He could have been hit by a car," said Claudia.

"He could have wandered off," said Mary Anne. "You know, the brook's not frozen over yet. What if he fell in?"

"There are worse things," I added. "What about all the missing kids these days? Someone could have driven by and just scooped him into a car. On a day like this"—I waved my hand around to indicate the disgusting weather—"there probably wouldn't be anyone around to see it happen. The person wouldn't even have to bother trying to *lure* Jamie into the car. He could just—kidnap him."

"That's *awful*," exclaimed Kristy.

"I know."

"Well, I think now we have to do something about the agency. Something more than just telling kids to talk to their parents. The question," Kristy said gravely, "is what? Maybe we should talk to our own parents. My mum usually knows what to do."

"I don't see what the problem is," said Claudia. "If I knew where Mrs Newton was I'd call her right now and tell her about Jamie. Then I'd call everyone else I could think of."

We had reached Kristy's house and were

standing in front of it, shivering and talking.

"No," I said. "I know what Kristy means. If we start calling parents who use the agency, they'll just think we're poor sports, and that we're trying to make the agency look bad because they're taking our business away."

"Oh," said Claudia. "Right."

"Well, let's just go home," Mary Anne suggested. "Maybe we *should* talk to our parents. The important thing is that Jamie's safe for now."

"All right," Kristy agreed uncertainly.

Claudia, Kristy, and Mary Anne went into their houses, and I walked the rest of the way home. I found my mother in the kitchen, reading the paper and having a cup of coffee. "Hi, sweetie," she greeted me. "How was school?"

"Fine. . . . Mum?"

"Yes?"

I had hung up my coat and was pouring myself a glass of milk. I sat down next to her at the table. "If you knew that someone was doing something that could put someone else in danger, what would you do about it?"

Mum looked at me thoughtfully. "I think I need a little more information," she said.

"Well, what if the someone who would be in danger was a little kid, and the someone putting him in danger was someone his

421

parents trusted, but if you told, you would look bad?"

"Stacey Elizabeth," my mother said sharply. "You're not talking about child abuse, are you?"

"Oh, *no*. Nothing like that."

I could see the relief in Mum's eyes. "And," she asked, "are you talking about any of the girls in your baby-sitting club?"

"No. I swear, I mean, the person *caus*ing the trouble isn't in the club."

"All right. Well, what do you mean about making someone look bad?"

"Making someone look like a poor sport or a tell-tale. What's the expression Dad uses?"

"Sour grapes?"

"Yeah. That's it."

"This is just my opinion," said Mum, "because you haven't given me the facts. But offhand, I'd say the person who's going to tell something should risk 'looking bad,' if a child really is in danger. There doesn't seem to me to be any question about it. Even if it's a difficult thing to do."

I nodded. "Okay. Thanks, Mum."

I ran upstairs to my parents' bedroom and phoned Kristy.

"I called my mother at work," she told me, "and she said the same thing your mum did, only I told her the whole story. Mary Anne hasn't got hold of her father, but Claudia talked to Mimi and *she* said the

422

same thing, too." (Claudia discusses all her problems with Mimi. She and Mimi are very close.)

"Well?" I asked.

"Well . . ." Kristy gulped. "I just saw Mrs Newton's car drive by. She's home. I guess it's now or never."

Fifteen minutes later, we met on the Newtons' front steps. Nobody wanted to ring the doorbell. After a lot of shuffling around, Claudia finally did it.

Jamie answered the door. "Hi-hi, again," he said. Mummy's home now!" He sounded absolutely delighted.

"Good," said Claudia. "Your mummy is just the person we want to see."

Mrs Newton ushered us into the living room. "You look very serious," she said. "Is anything wrong?"

"Actually, yes," said Kristy. She glanced at Jamie who was trying to climb into his mother's lap. "Could we talk to you alone?"

"Well . . . certainly." Mrs Newton looked surprised. I couldn't blame her. "Jamie," she said, "go see if *Sesame Street* is on, honey. Okay?"

Jamie left the room.

"We don't exactly know how to tell you this," Kristy began awkwardly, "but I guess we should begin with what happened this afternoon." She glanced at us.

Mrs Newton nodded patiently.

"Well, um, we were walking home from school, and when we got to your house we found Jamie playing outdoors."

"By himself," Mary Anne added.

"Near the street," Claudia added.

"With no hat or mittens," I added.

"He told us Cathy Morris was baby-sitting for him," Kristy continued. "But she was indoors. We don't think she knew where Jamie was. . . . We felt you really ought to know."

Mrs Newton didn't say a word. She looked horrified.

"We're sorry to be such tell-tales," I said nervously, "but we—"

"No, no. Oh, girls, I appreciate your telling me. I'm sure it was hard to do. I'm just—I can't believe—I mean, that was so irre*spon*sible."

I decided to go ahead and tell all. "I knew yesterday that Jamie hasn't liked his new baby-sitters, but we didn't want you to think we were bad-mouthing our competition. Jamie told me that most of his new sitters just talk on the phone or watch TV. He thought *I* wasn't going to pay any attention to him, either. And one of the sitters smokes, and burned a hole in the chair downstairs. Charlotte Johanssen has been upset, too. We had a long talk about it last night. She says one of her sitters invites her boyfriend over."

"Well," said Mrs Newton briskly, "I

certainly won't use the agency any more, although we did find one seventeen-year-old sitter we like very much. I'll continue to call him on his own, but not the others. I have to admit that Jamie hasn't seemed very happy lately, but I blamed it on sibling rivalry—the new baby. Anyway, I'll phone Peggy Johanssen and a few other parents. They'll want to know what you told me. And then I'll call Michelle and Liz, both of them. And Cathy Morris, of course. I wish I knew which one was the smoker."

"Mrs Newton," Kristy said suddenly, "I know you'll want to call Cathy about this afternoon yourself, but could you let us talk to Liz and Michelle? We have a score to settle with them."

13th CHAPTER

We settled the score first thing the next morning. We marched off to school and planted ourselves outside Liz and Michelle's classroom.

The girls arrived early.

"Well," said Liz." Look who it is. The Baby Club."

"Like, ha-ha," Kristy replied.

I giggled. Michelle scowled.

"Have you finally come crawling?" Liz asked. "When your club fails, you can always work for us, you know."

"No way," said Kristy. "We're here to talk to you about an important business matter."

"Yeah," I said.

"And what is so important?"

"What is so important," said Kristy, "is that yesterday Cathy Morris was baby-sitting for a three-year-old boy and she let

426

him go outdoors by himself."

"So?"

"So?! We found him playing near the street—with no hat or mittens. We had to send him inside. If we hadn't come along, he might have been hit by a car. Three-year-olds cannot play outside by themselves. And good baby-sitters ought to know that."

"So we won't give Cathy any more jobs," Michelle spoke up. "She doesn't really like baby-sitting anyway."

"That's no surprise," said Claudia.

"What do you mean by that?" snapped Liz.

"I mean," said Claudia, "that the kids *we* know don't like the sitters *you* find."

"Are you saying we're not good baby-sitters?" asked Michelle.

"Well," I said, "a good baby-sitter spends time with the children she sits for. She doesn't ignore them and talk on the phone or just watch TV all time."

"Oh, we *al*ways play with the kids we take care of. We tell the other sitters to do that, too. Right, Michelle?"

"Oh, *right*."

"Then," said Kristy, "you must know the kids pretty well by now. A good baby-sitter knows a lot about the children she takes care of. Do you know what Jamie Newton's favourite kind of sandwich is?"

Liz paused. "I only baby-sat for him once," she said.

"It's peanut butter and honey, toasted," said Mary Anne, finding her voice.

"What's Charlotte Johanssen's favourite TV programme?" asked Kristy.

Liz and Michelle glanced at each other. "*Mister Rogers*," Michelle said triumphantly.

"Michelle, Charlotte Johanssen is almost eight years old. Her favourite programme is *The Cosby Show*."

"Have you ever sat for the Marshalls?" asked Claudia.

"*I* have," said Liz. "Two girls: Nina, three, and Eleanor, one." (I really thought she was going to add, "So there.")

"Right," said Claudia. "And do you know what it means when Eleanor rubs her ears?"

"That she has an earache?"

"No, it means she's getting hungry."

"Do you remember what Nina is allergic to?" asked Mary Anne.

"For heaven's sake, what is this—Twenty Questions?"

"Come on," said Kristy. "You sat for her. I'll give you a hint. It's a food. What could you have fed her that would have made her break out in a rash?"

"I don't know, okay?" Liz said angrily, at the same time that Mary Anne said, "Strawberries."

"What are you trying to prove?" asked Michelle. But she answered her own

428

question. "That you're better baby-sitters than we are?"

"You said it, I didn't," replied Kristy.

"Okay, so you proved it," said Liz. "Now go away and leave us alone."

We did. We gathered in the girls' toilet. "What do you think that meant?" I asked.

The other club members shook their heads. It had felt like some sort of victory, but we weren't sure. We wondered what had happened when Mrs Newton called Cathy. We wondered what was going to happen when the parents heard the news about the agency and began talking to their children. We figured we'd hear something over the weekend.

Unfortunately, I was spending that important weekend in New York. My parents picked me up after school on Friday. I was all set. I had packed my bag the night before, and it was in the backseat along with a pillow, a Judy Blume book, an apple, and homework assignments for the following week. More important, I had seen Dr Johanssen the night before and a special doctor's appointment had been arranged for late Saturday afternoon. Before I left, she had handed me an official-looking envelope with my parents' names typed on the front.

I waved to Claudia, Mary Anne, and Kristy from the car window. "See you on Wednesday!" I called.

My father pulled away from the kerb and we began the two-hour drive to New York City. When we reached the highway, I said, "So who are we staying with this time—Aunt Beverly and Uncle Lou or Aunt Carla and Uncle Eric?" I hoped it was Aunt Beverly and Uncle Lou. I liked my cousins Jonathan and Kirsten a lot better than my cousin Cheryl.

Mum and Dad looked at each other and smiled. Then Mum turned around and faced me. "We were going to surprise you when we got to the city, but we might as well tell you now. We're not staying with the Spencers *or* the McGills."

"Yippeee! You mean we're staying in a hotel?" I adore hotels.

"No. . . . We're staying with the Cummingses. You can see Laine again."

"With the *Cum*mingses!" I exclaimed. "Do they know what's wrong with me, then? Did you tell them?"

"Yes, we finally told them. It's funny—now that you're so much better, there doesn't seem to be any reason for them *not* to know."

"Does Laine know?"

"Yes. The Cummingses have told her."

"But Mum, how could you do that to me? You know Laine hates me. And I hate her."

"Oh, Stacey," said Mum, "That was months ago. I'm sure you and Laine are over that fight especially now that Laine

430

knows the truth about you."

I slumped down in my seat. "No, we're not," I replied.

"Well, I'm sure you'll feel differently when you see her."

"No, I won't."

Laine didn't either. When Mrs Cummings opened the door to their flat and let Mum and Dad and me in, Laine wasn't in sight. Mrs Cummings greeted us warmly and showed Mum and Dad into the guest room where they would be staying. Then she told me to go on into Laine's room. I walked slowly down the hall to her bedroom. Being in the Cummingses' apartment felt strange after such a long time.

Laine's door was closed. A big sign said: KNOCK BEFORE ENTERING.

I knocked.

"Who is it?" Laine called.

"It's Stacey."

No answer.

"Can I come in?"

No answer.

I went in anyway. I threw my duffel bag down on one of the twin beds.

Laine was lying on the other bed, reading a book. She didn't look up.

I walked back to the door. "I just want you to know," I said as I started to close the door, "that I'm not any happier to be here than you are to have me. I wanted to stay in a hotel. In fact, staying with Cheryl would have been a picnic compared to this."

Laine finally looked up from her book. "Stacey—"

But I stepped into the hall, slamming the door behind me. I could hear the adults in the living room, so I went into the guest room. It was the only place I could be alone.

Laine and I didn't speak all evening. I noticed, though, that she watched me very carefully, especially at dinner. But there wasn't much for her to see. I cleaned my plate. Dessert was fruit, which I could eat. When I needed to give myself an injection of insulin, I did it quickly in the bathroom. I'm not sure what Laine was expecting that night, but I didn't faint or throw up, I was neither overweight nor underweight, and nobody gave me any special attention, food or favours.

I was as normal as she was, except that I had a disease called diabetes.

The next morning, my parents and I left for Dr Barnes' clinic around eleven o'clock. We wanted to enjoy the city, so we decided to walk. We walked down Central Park West with the park on our left, and then we turned onto West Sixty-Third Street.

The clinic was not far away. It occupied a suite of rooms on the ground floor of a tall modern block of flats. Mum gave our names to a receptionist in the waiting room and we sat down on a hard couch. We were the only people there.

Fifteen minutes late, a nurse entered the room. She told my parents that Dr Barnes would be with them shortly. Then she led me down a hall and into a examining cubicle.

And the tests began.

I was examined, poked, and prodded. Blood was drawn. I was fed a specially prepared lunch and more blood was drawn. Then this woman holding a sheaf of papers asked me to do weird things like draw a picture of my family, make up stories about inkblots, and build towers of blocks. I ran on a treadmill and tried to do sit-ups and push-ups. I rode an exercise bicycle. At last I was given a written test. It might have been an IQ test, but I wasn't sure. Whatever it was, it looked long. My appointment with the other doctor was at five o'clock, and I still hadn't even told my parents about it. At 3.10, I began to feel nervous. At 3.20, I began to perspire. But at 3.30, a nurse came to take the paper away. Whew! Just in time.

I was sent back to the waiting room. I had been at the clinic for four hours and I had not laid eyes on Dr Barnes.

My parents had, though, and they looked a little confused. I took advantage of that. I spotted a coffee shop across the street from the building the clinic was in. "Let's go get something to drink," I suggested.

When we were seated in a booth, Dad said, "Well, tell us about your day, honey."

I did—briefly.

The waitress brought our order.

As Mum and Dad sipped their coffee, I said carefully, "You know, you guys were right about something."

"What's that?" asked Mum.

"That it's important to learn about diabetes and do everything we can to try to overcome it or live with it better. And so . . . I've been looking into it myself."

"You have?" said Dad. "Good for you."

"Yeah. And I heard about this doctor, Dr Graham. He's a big authority on childhood diseases, especially diabetes. He's done lots of research and he even started some organization to study diabetes."

Dad raised his eyebrows and nodded his head.

"The thing is," I said, "I have an appointment with him today. It's sort of a . . . surprise. We're supposed to be at his office at five o'clock." I held out the letter from Charlotte's mother. "This is from Dr Johanssen. I think you better read it now."

"What?" my mother started to say. "Honey, I—"

"Just read it," I said. Dr Johanssen had shown me the letter before she sealed it in the envelope, so I knew what it said. It explained that we had discussed this new doctor and that I had expressed an interest

434

in seeing him and had asked Dr Johanssen to help me get an appointment. It said that I had gone to her confidentially, which was why she hadn't contacted my parents personally. She wound up by praising the doctor's work, apologizing to Mum and Dad for any inconvenience, and offering to talk with them when we returned to Stoneybrook.

My parents read the letter together, frowning.

"Stacey, I'm not quite sure what to think of all this," said Dad, when the letter had been returned to the envelope.

"I thought you'd be pleased," I said, although that wasn't quite true.

"Well, we are," said Dad. "We're just—we weren't expecting this. We don't know how expensive he's going to be. We don't know anything about him. I wish you'd discussed this with us before you made an appointment."

"You make appointments for me without asking me first," I pointed out.

"True . . ." said Mum. "Dr Graham. His name sounds familiar. . . . Philip Graham. I think I've heard about him or read about him." She began to look impressed. "He's supposed to be excellent, but very busy and almost impossible to see. You were lucky to get an appointment, Stacey."

"Listen," I said hastily, since Mum seemed so impressed, "his office is way across town at East Seventy-Seventh Street and York Avenue. We better get going."

Dad looked at his watch. "We certainly better." He paid the man at the cash register, and we hurried outside and hailed a cab.

I scrambled into the backseat between Mum and Dad. I crossed my fingers. So far, so good.

Dr Graham's office looked just the way I thought the office of a children's doctor should look. The waiting room was small and cosy, with two big, dumpy couches and lots of child-size chairs. On a little table by a window were some puzzles, a stack of picture books, and several copies of *Cricket* magazine. In a big bin were trucks, cars, dolls, and other toys. I sat down with the latest issue of *Seventeen*, and began to read while Mum spoke to the receptionist. In a moment, Dr Graham himself came out. He was a tall black man with sparkling eyes and a deep voice. I liked him right away.

"Well, Stacey," he said, shaking my hand, "I'm glad to see you. You're my last patient today. These must be your parents."

Mum and Dad and the doctor introduced themselves while Dad tried to apologize for my setting up the appointment without telling them about it.

Dr Graham said he didn't mind at all. Then he ushered us into his office, which was every bit as fancy and as full of diplomas as I could have hoped. "I'm not going to examine Stacey," he said. "This is a consultation only. I just want to ask some questions."

Some questions! He asked a billion. He asked about my birth, my health before the diabetes was discovered, the course of the disease, and how we were treating it. He asked about the doctors I'd seen, and my new doctor in Stoneybrook. He asked me how I was doing in school, how I had adjusted to the move, and whether I was making friends. Finally, he asked my parents to leave the office, and then he asked me some personal questions about how I felt about my doctors, my disease, and even Mum and Dad.

We talked forever, and he wrote down everything I said on a pad of yellow paper. Then he called my parents back into the office.

"Well," Dr Graham said to them, "you must be very proud of your daughter. I'm sure you feel lucky to have her."

My parents nodded, smiling. "In more ways than one," added Mum.

"I'm glad you realize that," replied Dr Graham, returning their smile, "because from what you've told me, Stacey was a pretty sick young lady, but she's made an excellent adjustment with the treatment that's been worked out for her. Quite honestly, without doing any tests, I can see

437

only one problem."

My mother paled slightly.

"What's that?" Dad asked nervously.

"Although Stacey has taken the move to Connecticut and the change of schools and friends in stride, she seems to feel quite unsettled about her disease. She wants to be able to have some control over it, but she's a little afraid of it, is that right, Stacey?"

"Well. . . ." I twisted my hands together. It wasn't easy to be with my parents and watch their reactions to what the doctor and I were saying. "I guess. I mean, the thing is, every time I think I understand what's going on, we see some other doctor who tells us to do something different. . . . I asked Dr Johanssen about Dr Barnes and his clinic. She said Dr Barnes might make me go to a psychiatrist, and even change schools." I had to pause and take a deep breath because I felt like I was going to cry. "I don't want to change schools again. I want to stay with Claudia and Kristy and Mary Anne. And I don't want to go to a psychiatrist or start exercise classes or anything else."

There were a few seconds of silence.

Then Dr Graham spoke quietly. "Dr Werner is a superb physician," he said. "She has a wonderful reputation, and is highly respected. It's my opinion that Stacey couldn't be in better hands—unless they were my own," he added, smiling.

Mum and Dad laughed, but they didn't

say anything for a moment. I saw them looking around the office at the diplomas and certificates and awards.

Dad cleared his throat. "I must admit," he said, "that we were a bit perplexed today by some of the things—"

"Many of the things," my mother interrupted.

"—many of the things Dr Barnes told us. The tests that he's recommending for Monday and Tuesday seem rather . . . unusual. And they're very expensive. Of course, money is no object where Stacey's health is concerned," he added hastily.

"Dr Graham?" asked Mum. "What do you know about Dr Barnes' clinic?"

Dr Graham didn't mince words. "I think it's a lot of bunk. Nothing he'll do will harm Stacey, but I don't think any of it is necessary. It's my opinion that what Stacey needs is some stability. What's most important for her right now is to understand her disease, and she can't do that if each doctor she sees tells her to try something different.

"As I said, I haven't done any tests, but Stacey seems incredibly healthy, considering how ill she was a year ago. And that comes from one thing only: regulating the amount of insulin in her body. As you know, the best way to do that is through insulin injections and diet, both of which Stacey seems to have worked out."

Mum and Dad looked at each other. They looked at me. "Maybe," said Mum, "it's time Stacey had some more say about her treatments. Do you want to go back to the clinic on Monday?" she asked.

"No," I said, "but I *would* like to see Dr Werner while we're here. Just for a check-up, if we can get an appointment on Monday."

"You mean you haven't already made one?"

"No," I said, giggling. "And after that we can go *home*, back to school and my friends and the Babysitters Club."

"Well," said Dad, "we'll discuss it tonight."

Everyone stood up then, and began shaking hands. I thanked Dr Graham, and he winked at me and wished me good luck and told me I could call him any time I had questions. He gave me a card with his phone number on it.

And that night we talked, Mum and Dad and I. They didn't leave me out of the discussion. We ate an early dinner in a restaurant and talked for two hours. The decision? No more Dr Barnes. Mum and Dad hadn't liked him anyway. They said they couldn't promise they'd never take me to some new doctor, but they agreed to hold off for a while, and to let me help make decisions in the future. "Why not?" I said, wolfing down my dinner. "I seem healthy, don't I?"

"As a horse," agreed Dad.

14th
CHAPTER

After dinner, we met Mr and Mrs Cummings and Laine, and the six of us went to a film. We reached the cinema a little late and couldn't all sit together. Laine and I ended up by ourselves in the back row. We agreed to meet our parents in front of the cinema when the film was over.

While the previews were showing, Laine got up and tiptoed into the lobby. She returned a few minutes later with a cola and a bag of peanuts.

"Thanks for asking if *I* wanted something," I whispered huffily.

Laine looked at me in surprise. "You? I thought you couldn't eat any of this stuff."

"I can eat popcorn. I can drink diet lemonade."

"Well, I didn't know that."

"You would if you ever bothered to speak to me."

441

"You—"

"Shhh!" The man in front of Laine turned around and glared at us.

Laine lowered her voice. "You don't talk to me, either. You never even told me the truth about your—your sickness."

"Why would I want to talk to someone who ignores me and turns our friends against me and—"

"SHHH!" The man turned around again.

The woman next to him turned around, too. "The movie is starting," she said, "and I'd like to hear what's going on."

I stood up. "Will you please let me by, Laine?" I asked super-politely. "I'd like to get something to eat."

I stalked out of the dark cinema—but I wasn't alone. Laine was right behind me. I ignored her and stepped up to the snack counter. "A small diet lemonade and a small popcorn, please," I said.

"That'll be a dollar seventy-five," replied the boy behind the counter.

I gulped. I'd forgotten how expensive things were in New York. At the cinema in Stoneybrook, you can get a lemonade and popcorn for ninety-five cents.

The boy pushed my order across the counter.

"Here you go."

I unfolded a dollar bill. It was the only money I had.

I blushed furiously.

"Here's seventy-five cents." Laine dropped three quarters into the boy's out-stretched hand.

"Thanks," I mumbled.

"Stacey?" Laine said, as I turned around, carrying my food.

"Yeah?"

"I'm sorry."

She didn't have to say what she was sorry about. I knew. "You are?"

"Yeah."

"I'm sorry, too. I guess I should have told you what was wrong, but Mum and Dad weren't telling anyone but family. . . . How come you stopped being my friend?"

Laine looked at her feet. "I don't know." She sat down on a chair outside the entrance to the ladies' cloakroom.

I sat down next to her, trying to balance the lemonade and the container of popcorn.

"I mean, I do know, I think. This is going to sound funny, but I was jealous."

"*Jealous*? Of *me*? You wanted to be sick?"

"Well, no. Of course not. I think if I had known what was wrong, I would have acted different. But you were getting so much attention. The teachers were always asking how you felt and giving you extensions on our assignments. And you got to miss so much school."

"Laine, I nearly had to stay back."

"You're kidding. I didn't know that. . . . Well, anyway," she went on, "remember

Bobby Reeder?"

I nodded.

"He said he thought you were contagious. I don't know why I believed him, but I did. And since I was your best friend, I was *positive* I was going to get it, whatever it was. I was so scared. I just didn't want to be around you any more. When my mother and father finally found out about our fight, they were sort of mad. We talked about it, but I didn't know how to apologize to you. That's why I never wrote after you moved to Connecticut. Besides, I didn't think you'd accept my apology. If *I* were you, I wouldn't want *me* for a friend."

I giggled. "Well," I said after a moment, "I *was* pretty mad. You did some mean things. But I guess it would have helped if I'd told you the truth. You know, lately I've been remembering New York a lot. And every now and then, I've thought, 'Gosh, I wonder if Laine would know. . . .' A couple of times I almost decided to write you a letter."

"What kinds of things were you wondering about?"

"Well, for instance, remember Deirdre Dunlop, and how we always said she'd be the first one in our class to outgrow her training bra? So, I was wondering—did she?"

Laine laughed, nearly choking on her cola. "Yes!" she exclaimed. "And remember Lowell Johnston?"

"Yeah."

"The day Deirdre came in wearing her new bra, he asked her for a date."

"You're kidding!"

"No. Honest. Cross my heart."

I kept asking questions and Laine kept answering them. I realized how much I had missed her.

The next thing we knew, people were pouring out of the cinema and into the lobby. We'd missed the whole film!

"Oh, well," I said to Laine. "It was worth it. We can see this film any time, but on Monday, I'll be leaving."

We tossed our empty cups and boxes into a bin and waited in front of the cinema for our parents.

That night, Laine and I talked until 2.30. We were tired the next morning, but we wanted to make the most of our day. We ate breakfast by ourselves at Leo's Coffee Shoppe around the corner from Laine's apartment building. Then we took a walk in Central Park. In the afternoon, the Cummingses and Mum and Dad and I went to *Paris Magic*. It was the best musical I'd ever seen. Afterwards, we ate dinner at one of my favourite restaurants, Joe Allen's.

When we got back to Laine's flat, she and I wanted to have another night of secrets and chitchat, but Mrs Cummings said,

"Lights out at ten o'clock," since Laine had to go to school the next day. By the time we went to sleep, I felt as if two huge weights had been lifted from my chest. One weight was the fight with Laine. The other was Dr Barnes and his clinic. I didn't have to worry about either one any more.

Mum called Dr Werner's office early Monday morning. The receptionist said she could squeeze me in between patients, so I saw Dr Werner at 10.30. She said I was doing fine.

And then we went home. I couldn't believe how happy I was to see Stoneybrook again. And I couldn't wait for school to let out so I could talk to the other members of the Babysitters Club. Luckily, I didn't have to wait long.

As soon as I saw kids riding their bikes up my street, I called the Kishis.

Mimi answered the phone.

"Hi, Mimi," I said. "It's Stacey."

"Stacey! You are at home? Claudia said that you would not be back until Wednesday. Everything is all right, I hope."

"Oh, yes! It's fine. Great, in fact! I'm glad to be home. Is Claudia back from school yet?"

"She is just walking in the door. Please wait and I will call her to the phone."

"Hello?" said Claudia, after several seconds.

"Claud, it's me, Stacey! I'm back early!

I'm finished with Dr Barnes. Did anything happen over the weekend? Did you go to the mall? Did any parents call Liz or Michelle?"

"Quite a few," Claudia replied smugly. "Charlotte and Jamie and the other kids told their parents everything. You should have seen the faces those girls put on in school today! If looks could kill, you'd be the only member of the Babysitters Club left."

"Wow," I said, giggling.

"I think our meeting this afternoon will be pretty interesting."

"Can I come over now? I can't wait any longer."

"Sure!"

I ran right over to Claudia's house. On the way, I passed Sam Thomas. I realized I'd barely thought about him recently. I'd been too wrapped up in doctors and the Babysitters Club. Besides, I was looking forward to going to the Snowflake Dance with Pete Black.

"Hi, Stacey!" Sam called.

"Hi, Sam!" I replied, and ran on.

Claudia met me at her front door and we went upstairs to her room. The girls had not, as it turned out, gone to the mall with their sandwich boards. Too much had been happening with the Baby-sitters Agency and the angry parents. They had decided to try to go the next weekend—if it was even necessary.

The phone began ringing at 4.30, an hour before our meetings start. Kristy and Mary Anne hadn't arrived yet. I answered the first call. It was Mrs Newton. "Hi, Stacey," she said. "I'm holding a meeting of the Literary Circle at my house on Friday afternoon, and I need someone to watch Lucy and keep Jamie busy for a couple of hours."

Watch Lucy! I was thrilled. "Oh, I'll do it!" I said. "What time?"

"Three-thirty to five-thirty."

"Great! I'll be there."

"By the way, Stacey, I thought you'd like to know that I had a talk with Cathy Morris. I hope I wasn't too hard on her. I explained all the responsibilities that are involved in baby-sitting and told her how upset I was about last week. I think she honestly didn't realize what she was doing wrong. She also told me she just found an after-school job at Polly's Store. She seems excited about it."

"Well, good," I said. "She'll probably earn more money that way."

"I also called the Johanssens, the Marshalls, the Pikes, the Spencers, the Gianmarcos, the Dodsons, and even Kristy's mother, just in *case* she would ever think of using the agency for David Michael. All the parents agreed that, if nothing else, they ought to know their baby-sitters in advance, and not trust the agency to find sitters for them. And I heard a number of complaints from other parents. Jamie and Charlotte weren't the only unhappy children. I want you to know how grateful we are that you girls were brave enough to come forward and tell us what was going on."

"Well," I said, "it wasn't easy, but I'm glad we did it."

A minute later, I got off the phone and began bubbling over with everything Mrs Newton had said.

But Claudia just glared at me.

"What?" I said. "What's the matter?"

"Stacey, you took that job Mrs Newton offered. You know the rules."

Oops. "Oh, yeah," I said. "Sorry." The rule is that every job that comes along must be offered to all the members of the club before someone takes it. I had just broken one of our most important rules.

"I'd like to take care of Lucy, too, you know," said Claudia. "And I bet Kristy and Mary Anne would feel the same way."

"I'm sorry," I said again. "I just forgot. I was so excited."

"Oh, it's okay," replied Claudia. "I'd be pretty excited if *I* were you. Besides, I've broken the rule often enough myself."

I grinned. That was true.

During the next half hour, both Mrs Marshall and Mr Johanssen called with last-minute jobs they had had agency sitters lined up for, but had cancelled over the weekend.

Kristy and Mary Anne arrived. We were offered four more jobs. One was with a new client. At six o'clock we got off the phone.

"I wonder if anybody will call us at home tonight," said Mary Anne.

"Probably," answered Kristy. "With Christmas so close, everybody is going to parties, dinners, concerts. . . . This may be our busiest season."

"Well," I said, it's been tough, but we hung in there and beat out the agency."

"More important," added Kristy, "we beat them because we're *good* baby-sitters."

"We won the battle *and* the war," said Mary Anne.

"We're the best!" exclaimed Claudia.

"I feel like we need a cheer," I said. "You know, 'Rah, rah, rah! Sis, boom, bah! . . . Something . . . something . . . The Babysitters Club! Hurray!"

"Would you settle for junk food?" asked Claudia. She removed a bag of gumdrops (and a bar of diabetic chocolate for me) from under the cushion of her armchair. "We ought to congratulate ourselves and celebrate."

The four of us looked at each other. "Congratulations," we said solemnly.

"We made it," I added.

Claudia passed around the food.

15th CHAPTER

Ring, ring.

"Hello?"

"Hello . . . Stacey?"

"Yes. . . . Laine, hi! Oh, I'm so glad you called. Hang on just a sec, okay?" I rested the phone on the kitchen table. "Mum, it's Laine. I'm going to talk to her in your room, okay? Could you hang up the phone when you hear me get on?" I raced upstairs and closed the door to my parents' bedroom. "I'm on, Mum." I heard a click as she hung up the phone. "All right, now we can talk," I told Laine. "So what's going on?"

"Well, I wanted to know what happened with your baby-sitting club. Last weekend, you said something was going on with some agency."

"Oh, you won't believe it! The agency went out of business!"

"You are kidding me!"

"No, honest," I said. "The parents stopped calling the agency because they decided they couldn't trust Liz and Michelle —you know, those two girls—to find good sitters. But guess what? Okay, so Claudia tells me this on Monday. We go to school on Tuesday and there's Liz, standing on the lawn carrying a sign that says Make-overs Inc., and next to her is Michelle with a bunch of fliers. She's passing them out, and Kristy, the chairman of our club, is so curious, she goes and takes one even though Michelle is looking at Kristy like she's a snake or a roach or something."

Laine giggled.

"We read the flier," I continued, "and Liz and Michelle *already have a new business*! You call them and pay them five dollars, and they show you how to put on make up, figure out the best way to fix your hair, that kind of thing. It's perfect for them, since that's all they care about. Then, for another five dollars, they'll take you shopping and help you pick out new clothes and jewellery and stuff. They even have special rates before school dances and holidays. Those girls are smart, Laine. They'll probably earn more money doing that than lining up sitting jobs for their friends.

"Oh, gosh, I went on. "I have so much to tell you! Yesterday, I got to sit for Lucy Newton, the new baby I told you about."

"Really?" squealed Laine. "You got to *sit* for her?"

"Well, sort of. Her mother was at home, but I did watch her and her brother for two hours while Mrs Newton held a meeting. And I got to hold her and give her a bottle. It was great! I can't wait until I can really baby-sit for her. Oh, and you know what else?"

"What?"

"Remember Charlotte Johanssen, the little girl who's having trouble with the kids at school?"

"Yeah?"

"Well, her parents had a conference with her teacher and they've decided to skip her into third grade. The work in second grade is too easy for Charlotte and her classmates don't like her because she always does her assignments so fast and never makes any mistakes. Her teacher thinks she'll do better starting over in a new class where the kids don't know her, and the work will be more challenging. Charlotte seems really excited. She's going to switch to the new class after Christmas."

"Well, that's good. I really wish I could meet all these people, Stace. I feel like I know them alr—just a sec. . . . Stacey, my mum says I have to get off in two minutes."

"Oh, no!" I cried. "Well, wait. I'll talk fast. I went to the Snowflake Dance with Pete and we had a great time. I got a new

453

dress. And for Christmas Mum and Dad are going to give me a phone for my own room, just so I can call you! And I want to know exactly how many times Deirdre and Lowell have gone out, counting everything, even trips to the library. And what did you ask for for Christmas?"

"I—Mum says she has to use the phone. I've got to get off."

"But Laine, you didn't have time to tell me *anything* about you."

"I know."

"Hey, you'll be the first person I call when I get my phone."

"Okay! Great!" Laine dropped her voice to a whisper. "Mum doesn't know it, but I'm going to call you on Christmas Day, okay?"

"Terrific!"

" 'Bye Stacey."

" 'Bye! Thanks for calling."

"Talk to you soon."

"I can't wait."

"Me, neither."

"Me, neither."

"How are we going to end this?"

"I don't know."

"I miss you."

"I miss you, too."

"Now I *really* have to get off."

" 'Bye, Laine."

" 'Bye, Stacey."

We hung up. A huge grin spread across

my face. I had a great idea. If Laine ever came to visit me in Stoneybrook, I would make her an honorary member of the Babysitters Club.

The Babysitters Club

Need a babysitter? Then call the Babysitters Club. Kristy Thomas and her friends are all experienced sitters. They can tackle any job from rampaging toddlers to a pandemonium of pets. To find out all about them, read on!